James
by the Grace
of God

HUGH ROSS WILLIAMSON

James
by the Grace
of God

London
MICHAEL JOSEPH

First published by
MICHAEL JOSEPH LTD
26 Bloomsbury Street,
*London, W.C.*1
1955

Set and printed in Great Britain by Tonbridge Printers Ltd,
Peach Hall Works, Tonbridge, in Bembo twelve on fourteen
point, and bound by James Burn at Esher

To
Leo FitzPhilip A.A.

CONTENTS

7

'From that moment (the birth of the Prince of Wales) onward bursts and blooms such a foison of forgery, treachery and falsehood as perhaps no country had ever seen before and as certainly England had never known—with the King as the bewildered victim of those lies and false documents. Its atmosphere seems to have poisoned posterity itself, so that those who have written on this brief turmoil have lied upon it with a grand assurance astonishing even in academic historians.'

HILAIRE BELLOC: *James the Second*

'No man can choose the state of life in which he is placed or the demands that such a state makes on him. Holiness may be found on the throne, where most men agree it encounters the greatest difficulties.'

LOUIS LAVELLE: *The Meaning of Holiness*

I

The Prince of Wales

THE Queen was in labour. The June sun streamed
through the windows of the bedchamber, blazoning
the golden crowns embroidered on the canopy and
on the canary-coloured satin quilt of the great bed. The sides
were open and the foot-curtains drawn, so that all in the
room might witness the birth.

James was on the bed holding his wife. He was unshaven
and but partially dressed, for he had been up only a quarter
of an hour when they had fetched him back to her side.
Hastily giving orders for the summoning of the Queen
Dowager, the privy councillors and others who had the
right or privilege to attend, he had returned immediately to
the bedchamber. That was an hour and a half ago. More
than forty people had since crowded into the room, but all
as they came in found the King where he was now, oblivious
to everyone but Mary Beatrice.

She clung to his strength. About a quarter to ten she cried
out in great pain and James, as if conscious for the first time
of the witnesses, turned and called the Lord Chancellor.
Jeffreys came up to the bedside to show he was there.
Sunderland, with the rest of the privy councillors, followed

him. As they stood there, Mary Beatrice's hand pulled James's face down to her own.

'Stay like this.'

He did not understand what she meant.

'How?'

'Like this. With your head and periwig to hide my face. I will not see the men's eyes.'

So James stayed, screening her from the required intrusion, until the midwife announced the birth and gave a sign to the Countess of Sunderland, who put her hand up to her head, tidying an escaping curl. The gesture, unnoticed by any but those watching for it, told James that he had an heir.

As the Queen's sempstress, who had taken the child from the midwife, was passing by the bedside across the step to carry it into the little bedchamber beyond, the King stopped her and addressed the councillors: 'You are all witnesses that a child has been born. Follow into the next room and see what it is.'

As the wave of sound receded, James bent and kissed his wife on the mouth.

Between these two there was no need of words. They shared unspoken the same gratitude, the same fears, the same hope. Their last child, who had been born in that room on that bed six years ago, had lived only two months and was the fourth of their children to die in infancy. The memory of an earlier loss was still more potent. Their only son, Charles, born also in that room on that bed, had died from bad nursing, for when the physicians had opened the little body, they had agreed that, had proper care been taken, he should have lived many years. James had grieved more bitterly at his death than at that of any of his other children. Even now, eleven years later on this Trinity Sunday in the year 1688, the pain of it mingled with his gratitude that once more he had an heir.

Neither James nor Mary Beatrice doubted that the new child was a direct answer to prayer. The certainty and simplicity of their faith was still the strongest bond between this plain, obstinate Englishman of fifty-four and his vivacious Italian wife of thirty. It was stronger even than the friendship and understanding forged by the vicissitudes of the fifteen years of their politic marriage. Now all that Mary Beatrice said was: 'Give my thanks also,' and James, smiling assent, left her and made his way, with that quick, soldierly step of his, to the Queen's chapel across the courtyard of the palace.

Outside the chapel he met the Duke of Berwick, who was waiting there.

'A Prince of Wales?'

The King nodded.

'No one in England is more happy for you than I am.'

'I know that, James.'

'And I shall serve him, father, as I try to serve you.'

As he looked at the handsome, eighteen-year-old boy, already famous in Europe as a soldier, the King's reserve broke. He took him in his arms.

'He will inherit my throne, James; but not your place in my heart. You must believe that.'

James FitzJames, Duke of Berwick, was the eldest of the King's illegitimate children and, unchallengeably, his best loved.

'I will try to show myself worthy of it by saving his rights,' he said, returning the pressure of his father's arm. The stilted phrase did not mask the affection; but it was the practical man of action who added quickly: 'We shall need all our wits, sir. The dogs will be barking already.'

'We can tame them when it is time. Now there are other things to do.'

Berwick, who was not less devout than his father, went in with him to the chapel and the two Jameses knelt side by side before the Blessed Sacrament remembering the third who had just been born.

The dogs were indeed barking. The London mob had already been prepared, by those who managed it, for this birth. As soon as the Queen's pregnancy had been announced last January, ballads in the streets had appeared even before prayers in the churches, the former ridiculing the latter as attempts

> To rig out a thanksgiving
> Or a dainty fine prayer
> For a son and heir
> That's neither dead nor living.

The possible birth of a Prince of Wales was represented as a triumph for the Catholic Church which, good Protestants were reminded,

> consists of vicious Popes, the rest
> Are whoring nuns and bawdy, bugg'ring priests.
> A noble church! daubed with religious paint
> Each priest a stallion, every rogue a saint,

and exhorted

> Come you that loathe this brood, this murd'ring crew,
> Your predecessor well their mercies knew;
> Take courage now and be both bold and wise
> Stand for your laws, religion, liberties.
> You have the odds; the Law is still your own,
> They're but your traitors, therefore pull 'em down.

Rumours had been assiduously spread that the Queen was incapable of further childbearing. The uses of a cushion became the subject of interminable and intolerable jests. From Wapping to Westminster, in ale-house and coffee-house, men elaborated stories of the secret preparations afoot for smuggling a male child into the royal bedchamber at the appropriate moment, though there was some difference of opinion as to whether it was James's own bastard or whether its mother was a nun, lying-in in an adjacent room of the palace.

Of all this, James was aware. It neither surprised nor alarmed him. As long as he could remember, rebellion and calumny had been inseparable from kingship. Just after his ninth birthday, he had been with his father, Charles I, at the battle of Edgehill and seen subjects in arms against their King. At twelve he was a prisoner in the hands of the victorious rebels, who took him from his family, dismissed his household companions and would not allow even his harmless, favourite dwarf to remain to comfort him. Disguised as a girl he had at last managed to escape to his mother in France and here the news came that, on a January morning, they had killed his father on a scaffold in Whitehall. These things he had known as a King's son.

Nor did his experiences as a King's brother contradict the knowledge. He was twenty-six and a hardened soldier when the Restoration brought back to the throne of England his brother, the second Charles, mercurial, selfish, witty and consummately clever, with himself, as Duke of York, the heir-apparent. It should have been a golden age, but because of his religion, he had to go twice more into exile —and once he went, for all his fortitude, with tears— while the more pliant King patiently outmanœuvred the parliamentary millionaires who, in their determination to control the Crown, tried to exclude James from the succession.

They had, indeed, failed, but when he at last became King James II he had to sustain his title in arms once more against the nominee of the Faction, his brother's eldest bastard, the Duke of Monmouth; and though the open danger had been crushed at Sedgmoor and Monmouth had paid for his foolishness with his life, James knew in his bones that for him the contest with rebellion would never cease. Like his kingship, it was part of the burden of his inheritance. He had been born into an age which had challenged and overthrown the old sanctities. And he had been born with the duty to defend them. Those remote, heavy-lidded eyes of his had watched men steadily for nearly half a century and noted the greed and the grasp of the passion for power. Yet since he knew it from observation only and not from any answering weakness in his own nature, he was half-defeated before he fought.

In his private diary he noted: 'Nothing doth amaze and astonish me so much as to see many witty and ingenious men of most professions so industrious and diligent in pursuing their worldly and temporal advantage and so negligent and remiss in what concerns their eternal good, when every day we see that all we grasp at is vanity and vexation and that nothing but the love of God can fill and satisfy the heart of man.' What action he was capable of in the affairs of this world was comprehended in the circumference of courage. For him that was the virtue without which no other could be certain. The bravest of his house, he took physical courage for granted; but there were moments in which he feared that the temptations of policy might weaken his stand for the Faith. At the time of the Exclusion matter, his brother had asked him to let his Catholicism go by default—not, indeed, to renounce it, but not openly to practise it—in order to advance his popularity with the indifferent. Their grandfather, Henry of Navarre, had thought Paris worth a Mass. Was not London worth an abstention from it?

James answered: 'Think what a base thing it would be in me, besides the sin of it, to dissemble and deny my religion; I have by God's grace never to do so damnable a thing; and let my friends take their measures accordingly.'

And now that he was James, by the grace of God, King of England, Scotland and Ireland, he kept the same simplicity of defiance, even though he half-foresaw what the end must be. For his kingship and his faith, his duty to man and his duty to God, seemed to clash in a situation which was not simple and which no casuistry could make so. So all that he could ask of God was that the gift of a son might not subtly weaken his resolve to let the lesser thing go—to sacrifice his throne rather than his faith.

In St James's Church, the reading of the first lesson at morning prayer was just over. Henry Hyde, Earl of Clarendon, was nodding his approval of the probable appropriateness of the last verse to present discontents—'Then said I, Lord how long? and he answered, Until the cities be wasted without inhabitant and the houses without man and the land be utterly desolate'—when he noticed a considerable whispering among that part of the congregation which was near the door. Throughout the *Te Deum* he made what efforts he discreetly could to discover the cause of it, but as his position prevented him from actually sending his page out of the pew to ask, he had to possess his soul with what patience he could till the end of the service.

Even then, since it was beneath his dignity to inquire and no one volunteered any information, he was none the wiser and he was almost home before his page overtook him with the news that a Prince of Wales had just been born.

He did not believe it and said so.

The boy, however, was so definite that he sent his major-domo down to the Palace for certain confirmation or denial. By the time he had dined, the matter was put beyond doubt and he set out at once to offer his congratulations.

He found James shaving. After kissing his hand and wishing him joy, he apologized for not coming earlier. James made a counter-apology for his appearance but explained that the Queen had been so sudden and quick in labour and that, since the birth, he had had so much company that he had not had time to dress himself until now. After this exchange of courtesies, the brothers-in-law fell silent. Except on the subject of medals, which was their common hobby, they had never found small-talk easy and, at this particular moment, there was a vast area of implications which both wanted to avoid.

Consequently, when James suggested that he should go and look at the baby, Clarendon accepted with alacrity and was able to note later in his diary: 'My lady Powys (who was made governess) showed me the Prince; he was asleep in his cradle and was a very fine child to look upon.' If he refrained from adding, as some might have expected of him, that he was surprised not to have been invited to witness the birth, it was not for fear of committing an indiscretion in writing, but because he genuinely felt no surprise. He had been at Morning Prayer. James would know that he was at Morning Prayer and, even had there been time, would not have disturbed him at it. If the King had respect for nothing else in the Church of England, he never failed to defer to the scruples of one who, so the unkind said, preferred the company of Anglican bishops to any other form of human pleasure, and even occasionally imagined that he *was* the Church of England.

In point of fact, James's attitude to his brother-in-law had in it an element of paradox which Clarendon never suspected. It is true that he found him useful as a touchstone of what the Church of England was likely to think of any policy, but chiefly he regarded him as one of the main, if unwitting, instruments of his own leaving of it. His sister, Anne, James's first wife, had, shortly before her death seventeen years ago, begun to show considerable interest in the Catholic Faith. The many years of exile she had spent with her husband in France and Flanders had familiarized her with the atmosphere of Catholicism and she gradually became so impressed with the devotion of ordinary Catholics that—in her own words —'I made it my continual request to Almighty God that, if I were not, I might before I died be in the true religion. I had not the least doubt but that I was so and never had any scruple till November 1669.'

It was at this point that her brother had recommended her to read Dr Peter Heylin's *History of the Reformation*, telling her that if she had any doubt about her religion, 'that would settle her.'

It did. 'I found in it,' she wrote in her large, untidy hand, 'the description of the horridest sacrileges in the world and could find no reason why we left the Church but for three of the most abominable ones that ever were heard of among Christians. First, Henry VIII renounces the papal authority, because he would not give him leave to part with his wife and marry another in her lifetime. Secondly, Edward VI was a child and governed by his uncle who made his estate out of Church lands; and then Queen Elizabeth, who being no lawful heiress to the Crown, could have no way to keep it but by renouncing a church that could never suffer so unlawful a thing to be done by one of her children. I confess I cannot think the Holy Ghost could ever be in such councils.'

Her honesty made the conclusion inevitable. In spite of all obstacles—for quite apart from the political repercussions and the pressure put upon her by her own family, James himself was at that time an Anglican—she was received into the Church, inspiring her husband to follow shortly after her death the same path.

If James was thus bound to Clarendon by a thread of gratitude of which he was quite unaware, there was another tie which was patent enough. Anne Hyde might have died a Catholic and James might live as one, but—so it was decreed —their two children, Mary and Anne, must be safeguarded against contamination. Their education was taken out of their father's hands and entrusted to Henry Compton, Bishop of London, who saw to it that they were brought up not merely as Protestants but as bitterly hostile to their father's religion. Although James was, to the Princess Anne at least, an over-indulgent father, this barrier had remained; and in some matters he recognized, without jealousy, that her uncle Clarendon had more influence on her than he could hope to have.

It was natural that they should speak of Anne as soon as Clarendon returned from the Prince's bedchamber.

'I am sorry my niece is at the Bath,' he said.

'My regret is even greater,' answered James. 'I entreated her as earnestly as I could to wait till after the Queen's delivery.'

'So she told me. I advised it too. It would have been more seemly for her to have been here.'

'I was thinking rather of the Queen. I should have liked her to have had the comfort of Anne at such a time. They are like sisters.'

Into Clarendon's mind flashed: 'A little more than kin and

less than kind,' but he banished it immediately as being, perhaps, unjust to his niece. He had no tangible proof and he was not a man to foster his intuitions.

'Anne's doctor said it might be dangerous to her health to wait longer,' James continued, 'and, of course, as I told her, all other considerations must yield to that. She will be back this week. I am glad.'

'Then she might the more easily have returned a few days earlier,' retorted Clarendon.

His stubbornness on this point provoked an answering pertinacity in the King. James suddenly felt the need to justify his beloved daughter. 'She could not have foreseen this. Her duty to me is so great that, even at the risk of her health, she would have stayed had I not told her that the Queen had two reckonings and might well go a month longer. It was true, though unlikely.'

Clarendon bowed. He recognized the finality in James's tone. But today James did not wish to end frozenly. With a laugh, he added: 'So George will be able for once to ask his question with some show of intelligence.'

Clarendon gave an answering smile to this new turn of a family joke. Anne's husband, Prince George of Denmark, was without exception the most stupid man at Court. His habitual taciturnity, due less to his difficulty in expressing ideas than to his lack of any ideas to express, was regularly broken by the exclamation: 'Est-il possible?' Though his French was execrable and his accent affected he had managed to manipulate with some skill this one phrase which he found providentially suitable to almost any occasion. He was known privately as 'little Est-il-possible?'

'Poor George,' said Clarendon. 'I have often wondered if he enjoys his visits to the Bath.'

'It is possible,' said James.

The atmosphere was easy again. Clarendon took his leave with great friendliness. But he did not tell the King that he was now going to visit the seven bishops imprisoned in the Tower.

II

The Seven Bishops

THE names of the Seven were on everybody's tongue—
William Sancroft, Archbishop of Canterbury; Ken of
Bath and Wells and his life-long friend, Turner of
Ely; White of Peterborough and Lake of Chichester; Lloyd
of St Asaph and Trelawney of Bristol. When, two days
earlier, on the Friday evening, they had been taken from
Whitehall to the Tower in one of the King's barges, all
London, it seemed, had come out to greet them. On the
banks of the Thames, thousands had knelt to ask their
blessing; on the river itself were innumerable wherries whose
cheering occupants shouted as they passed: 'God save your
Lordships!'; many, unable to afford or procure oars, waded
waist-high into the water to show their enthusiasm.

But, for all that, the individuals matching the names were
known to few. 'The Seven Bishops' had become a collective
symbol of resistance. 'The Seven Bishops' had defied the
King. That was all the crowd knew or needed to know, at
least about five of them, though Sancroft the venerable
archbishop was a popular figure, loved for his charities at
Lambeth and Lloyd of St Asaph was remembered from the
days of the 'Popish Plot' ten years earlier. For the archbishop,

as head and leader, the cheers had a personal note; nor did those who gave them know that Sancroft, now in his seventy-second year, was in truth less a leader than a loyal, puzzled old man caught in a situation he could neither understand nor control and that the power lay with Lloyd, the domineering Welshman of sixty with the crazy eyes and powerful, jutting chin.

As a child, William Lloyd had been a prodigy of learning. Proficient in Latin and Greek and adequate in Hebrew at the age of eleven, he had at fourteen taken his degree at Oxford where in men's estimation his achievements rivalled those of the famous 'boy-bachelor,' Cardinal Wolsey. But his main preoccupation, even from those early days, had been with the more occult branches of learning—with astrology, numerology and the foretelling of the future. After leaving Oxford he took a post as tutor to the children of Backhouse, the Rosicrucian astrologer and here he first became friendly with Elias Ashmole, versed even more profoundly in the same arts. Later, his sister married into the Blagrave family which also boasted a famous astrologer.

Lloyd's own predictions were monotonously unfulfilled and by middle-life he could be not unjustly described as 'half-crazed by his persevering endeavours to extract from *Daniel* and the *Revelations* some information about the Pope and the King of France.' It may be that he was not sufficiently detached and single-minded in his occultism for he had also a strong vein of practicality which ensured that, even if he foresaw accurately nothing else, he contrived to foresee very well what was most profitable for his own interest. As an Anglican clergyman, he trimmed his sail to

every theological breeze, becoming indistinguishable from a
Presbyterian during the Presbyterian ascendancy and writing
a defence of High Church principles when the Restoration
made that the fashionable wear. Wealth and preferments
inevitably followed, and at the time of the Popish Plot he
found himself Prebendary of St Paul's and Rector of the
influential church of St Martin's-in-the-Fields. In this
capacity he was able to grasp the power of popularity as a
baiter of Catholics. With his instinct for showmanship, he
stationed two tall able-bodied clergymen on each side of the
pulpit of St Martin's to protect him from an imaginary
attempt at assassination while he used his native Welsh gift
of oratory in anti-Catholic sermons to whip up popular fury
to its fiercest. He became the benefactor of Titus Oates and
the patron of the perjurer Turberville, whose lies brought
the innocent to the scaffold. His power in London, linked to
theirs, became such that Charles the Second thought it
advisable to remove him from the scene of it by appointing
him Bishop of St Asaph.

There for the last eight years he had lived, writing and
printing his books, scheming incessantly, feeding his vanity
in various forms. Perfecting his occult practice, skilfully
publicizing his books, pestering the archbishop for preferment for his friends, he had yet one other outlet which no
one at all suspected. Through one of his Blagrave brothers-
in-law who was a chaplain at the Hague, he kept up a
continual correspondence with the heir-presumptive to the
throne, James's nephew and son-in-law, William, Prince of
Orange. He had—or so he imagined—the fate of the throne
itself in his hands, should events take a certain turn.

Yet even this reality of power seemed cold and unsatis-
fying by comparison with the emotional ecstasy of that
climacteric moment when the mob bayed its obedience. This
he had so missed during his Welsh exile that now, as he
passed down the river savouring it once more, he became a
little over-theatrical in his gestures of blessing the people.

Of the other six bishops, only one matched Lloyd in
unscrupulousness—Sir Jonathan Trelawney, Bishop of
Bristol. He was the youngest of them, a thirty-eight-year-old
Cornishman whose family had a tradition of loyalty to the
Crown. His father had been faithful in James's service; his
sister had been brought up at Court as playmate and friend
of the Princess Mary and he himself had fought for the
King at the time of Monmouth's rebellion. Here, indeed, he
had shown such energetic cruelty that, in popular legend,
his name was bracketed with those of 'bloody' Jeffreys and
the sadistic Kirke in a ballad which reminded men how he

> did his reeking heat assuage,
> On every signpost gibbet up his rage,
> Glutted with blood, a really Christian Turk
> Scarcely outdone by Jeffreys or by Kirke.

He considered he should have been adequately rewarded
for his exploits and that the inferior see of Bristol, worth a
mere £300 a year, was not adequate. As the King showed no
signs of remedying it, Trelawney became active in opposition
and was among the first to intrigue with William of Orange.
When that Prince sent his secret envoy to canvass opinions
about another rebellion, headed this time by himself in the
role of 'the Protestant champion,' Trelawney assured him of

his whole-hearted support and subsequently boasted: 'If King James sends me to the Tower, I know the Prince of Orange will come and take me out.'

To him, therefore, as to Lloyd, the journey to the Tower that evening of Friday, June 8, 1688, was the purposed prelude to greater things, though, as a soldier and a baronet, he regarded the kneeling crowds somewhat differently from the emotional Welshman.

At St James's Palace, the 'Seven Bishops' were hardly less vivid in thought to the King than their presence was to Clarendon as he became one with the vast crowd which, on Sunday afternoon, thronged their lodgings in the Tower. In spite of James's joy at the birth of an heir, in spite of the fact that the business to transact and audiences to give occasioned by it left him little time for musing, 'the Seven' hovered there, shadowing his happiness, mocking his plans. In the depths of his mind was the suspicion, though still elusive and unformulated, that they had caused him to mishandle a critical situation. It was not that he regretted his stubbornness. That sprang from his axiom that both his father's death and his brother's troubles had been due to their accommodating flexibility and that a King should never compromise. It was rather that he had neither foreseen nor intended a position in which such conduct would have been necessary and that the impasse had arisen not from his stubbornness but from the bishops'. Yet he still could not believe that the situation was purposed.

Sancroft, who owed the archbishopric to his influence as Duke of York, who had crowned him King, whom for the greater part of his life he had regarded as a friend, was an honest enough man. The sincere, good-natured Francis Turner, devotedly loyal to the Crown, his own official Anglican chaplain who knew him with the familiarity of long years spent in his private circle, who had shared his exile in Scotland, who had preached his Coronation sermon, was aware—none better—of the scrupulous honesty of his intentions toward the Church of England. Thomas Ken, though openly hostile to Catholicism, was still more opposed to the Protestantism of William of Orange as he had seen it in the days when he was at the Hague as Princess Mary's chaplain. Thomas White, Princess Anne's chaplain, and the Yorkshireman John Lake, recently translated from the see of Bristol to that of Chichester, seemed equally above suspicion. And though this could hardly be said of Trelawney, the present Bishop of Bristol, or of Lloyd of St Asaph, the one was too vehement and the other too crazed to have much influence with the others or to constitute a danger to the Crown.

When Clarendon left him—on his way, James had little doubt, to the Tower—he went over once more in his mind the circumstances which had led to the bishops' imprisonment.

The elements of the situation were simple. In his accession speech he had made a promise: 'I shall make it my endeavour to preserve this government, both in Church and State, as it is now by law established. I know the principles of the Church of England are for monarchy, and the members of it have shown themselves good and loyal subjects: therefore I shall always take care to defend and support it. I know too that the laws of England are sufficient to make the King as great a monarch as I can wish; and as I shall never depart from the just rights and prerogatives of the Crown, so I shall never invade any man's property. I have often heretofore ventured my life in defence of the nation and I shall still go as far as any man in preserving it in all its just rights and liberties.'

And he had kept his word. He had upheld the Church of England. He had interfered with no man's rights. All he had done was to extend the right to practise their own religion, to educate their children as they wished, to hold office in the State, to become magistrates, doctors, lawyers, to those of his own faith and to dissenters. The penal laws, which denied such rights to all but Anglicans, could not, he knew, be repealed without the consent of Parliament, but it remained a part of the Royal prerogative to dispense with these laws as an interim measure until Parliament should meet. They could be temporarily suspended by Royal edict and liberty of conscience be proclaimed.

Quite apart from the iniquity of making the reception of Holy Communion according to the Anglican rite the test of a man's right to earn a living and to serve his country, his own presence on the throne as a Catholic king made those laws patently absurd. As he had pointed out, it was not only 'highly unreasonable to punish men if they fortune to believe as the greatest part of the Christian world does,' but the laws, as they stood, 'made a criminal of the prince to the very government over which he presided by declaring the worship he makes use of to be idolatry, and (than which nothing could be more absurd) made him by embracing that faith, guilty of high treason against himself.' Mere common sense, as well as Christian charity, demanded a revision and two years after his coronation he had issued his edict of toleration, the Declaration of Indulgence. On the first anniversary of it, he had ordered that it should once more be read in all the pulpits of the land on two successive Sundays—in London on May 20 and 27; in other places on the 3rd and on this very 10th of June, 1688.

Though he knew that certain church dignitaries, fearful of infringements of their exclusive privileges, resented the Declaration, he was confident of the support of the Church of England as a whole; and for the moment it seemed there was no cause for apprehension. His order had been given on April 27 and it was not until ten o'clock at night on Friday, May 18—thirty-six hours before the reading of the Declaration was due to take place—that Sunderland came to his bedchamber to announce that six bishops urgently craved an audience to present him with a petition. They had come direct from Lambeth, but were not accompanied by Sancroft who, racked with a cough, preferred not to risk the night air.

James, assuming that they desired some slight modification in the wording of the Declaration, gave orders for them to be admitted and received them in the dressing-room leading out of the bedchamber, if not with affability at least with graciousness. They fell on their knees and Lloyd of St Asaph presented him with the petition which, as soon as he opened it, he recognized was in Sancroft's writing.

In silence he read that, in the name of all the bishops and clergy, they refused to read the Declaration the following

Sunday 'because that Declaration is founded upon such a dispensing power, as hath often been declared illegal in Parliament and is a matter of so great moment and consequence to the whole nation, both in Church and State, that Your Petitioners cannot in prudence, honour or conscience, so far make themselves parties to it.'

So direct and unforeseen an attack took him momentarily off his guard. His slow speech—for, like his father, he suffered from an impediment which produced a certain hesitancy—did not mask his anger.

'This is a great surprise to me,' he said. 'These are strange words, especially from some of you.' He looked from Turner to Ken. Then, his eyes returning to Lloyd: 'This is a standard of rebellion.'

Lloyd looked down his nose. It was Trelawney who protested with some over-emphasis: 'Rebellion! Sir, I beseech you, do not say so hard a thing of us. For God's sake, do not believe we are, or can be, guilty of rebellion. It is impossible that I, or any of my family, should be so.'

'We may hope it,' said James.

'Your Majesty cannot but remember,' continued Trelawney, 'that you sent me down into Cornwall to quell Monmouth's rebellion, and I am ready to do what I can to quell another, if there were occasion.'

'We rebel, sir?' echoed Turner—but his voice was quieter and more certain—'we are ready to die at your feet.'

Ken took a different line. 'Sir,' he said, 'I hope you will give us the same liberty which you wish to allow to everyone else.'

Lake seized on the point and reiterated it: 'Sir, you allow

liberty of conscience to all mankind. The reading of this Declaration is against our conscience.'

The protestations of loyalty and the insistence on conscience had the effect of increasing James's anger. He reflected that they had had three weeks in which to make their protests but that they had chosen to delay them till this eleventh hour, so that there was no time to discuss them properly or even, if he changed his mind, to countermand his order for the reading of the Declaration on Sunday. It looked to him as if they had spent the time in discovering what support they would get for their protest and, finding it in their power to whistle up the winds, had resolved to raise a storm.

'I will keep this paper,' said James. 'It is the strangest address I ever saw. It is an incitement to rebellion. You question my dispensing power! Some of you here have written and preached in favour of it when it suited your purpose.'

This accusation was true of them all. For quarter of a century the Church of England had preached, in season and out of season, the doctrine of non-resistance to the King. The great Jeremy Taylor, who had epitomized the doctrine in the memorable sentence: 'Obedience to Princes is the glory of the Protestant Religion' had gone further and insisted that even an unlawful edict ought to be published by the clergy if they were ordered to do so by a lawful prince. In support of this he had cited St Gregory who, when Mauritius directed him to publish in the churches a certain edict which he regarded as sinful, had remonstrated but obeyed.

The King now reminded the bishops of this and added: 'I

have much more reason to expect your compliance. What I ask you to publish is not sinful in itself. None of you would dare to say that freedom of conscience is a sinful thing. And I do not ask you to approve it or to recommend it to the people, but only to read it to them.'

This was unanswerable. Lake admitted: 'Sir, what we say of the dispensing power refers only to what was declared in parliament.'

'You are not speaking as members of parliament,' retorted James, 'but as bishops of the Church of England. The dispensing power was never questioned by the men of the Church of England.'

'The dispensing power,' said Lloyd, 'was declared against in the first parliament called by his late majesty and by that which was called by your majesty.'

'The dispensing power,' answered James, 'is not a matter for parliament; it is part of the prerogative. It was given me by God and I will maintain it.'

'We are bound to fear God and honour the King,' said Ken softly. 'We desire to do both. We will honour you. We must fear God.'

Trelawney seconded him. His crisp Cornish voice rapped out: 'We will do our duty to your majesty in everything to the utmost, provided it does not interfere with our duty to God.'

The standard of rebellion was firmly planted and James recognized it. He made a last appeal to Turner: 'Is this what I have deserved of you? I have supported you and the Church of England and will support it. And you have signed this paper.'

Lloyd stretched out his hand for the document, but James folded it and put it in his pocket. 'I shall keep this. I shall not part with it. I did not expect this from you, especially from some of you. But you will read the Declaration on Sunday.'

'God's will be done,' murmured Ken.

'What is that?'

'God's will be done,' repeated Ken loudly and joined, this time, by Lake.

There was nothing to be gained by continuing the argument. James dismissed them with: 'If I think fit to alter my mind, I will send to you. There are seven of you; but I tell you there are seven thousand—and of the Church of England, too—that have not bowed their knees to the Baal of rebellion.'

When they had gone, he read over the petition once more. After Sunday, he would have to take some decision about it, but, reflecting more calmly, he decided that the danger might be less than he had feared. The majority of bishops would remain obedient, the Declaration would be read and the generality of men would know nothing of the Petition and of the struggle of wills at Whitehall. By midnight, he was peacefully asleep and so knew nothing till the morning of the final blow. For at midnight, hawkers swarmed about the streets, rousing people from their beds, shouting 'News! News!' and selling printed copies of the Petition, of which the King had supposed the only copy was in his pocket. By morning it was the gossip of every coffee-house and the secret printer (who alone knew how the confidential document had come into his hands) had cleared a thousand pounds by a penny broadside.

The trap was perfectly sprung. All London now regarded the reading of the declaration in the churches next day as a political demonstration against the King and thus James was put in a position from which, even had he wished, he could not withdraw without seeming to betray his kingship. On Sunday, the churches were crammed to the doors, only to empty noisily where any clergyman dared to obey the Royal command. In most cases it was disobeyed.

On Monday, James went hunting. The gossips averred that this was his method of avoiding an interview with the archbishop, who waited on him in vain all day. Sancroft, to do him justice, was only a little less disturbed and indignant than the King himself at the publication of the Petition and realizing that he would be held responsible for it, though he neither knew of it nor could have prevented it, wished to make what amends he could. But James, who had been told this, was in no mood to receive him. The events of the last two days had destroyed his belief in the honesty of any of the Seven. He would see Sancroft in his own way and in his own time.

Yet it was not to avoid the meeting that he kept the arrangements he had made to hunt. He needed some strenuous bodily exercise to free him from the darkened closet of his mind, cobwebbed with conflicting counsels. In his youth, he had been one of the fiercest riders in England. Still, in his middle fifties, he rode so hard that he usually lost his company. His leaps were too dangerous for many to follow; he would lead his horse through a river, breast high, caring nothing for soaking clothes; if the wind was roaring a gale, he liked it the better. The old campaigner by sea and land, who had never had a day's illness in his life, replaced for this day of freedom the care-worn King. It was dark before he returned, having killed his stag in the mimic conflict and cleared his mind for decision in the more deadly game.

The bishops had lent their spiritual authority to further a political intrigue. Having appealed to Cæsar, to Cæsar they should go. The matter did not in fact and therefore should not in law concern the Church. They should be proceeded against in the ordinary secular courts on the charge of seditious libel.

The final decision when it was announced appeared to emerge from the debates of statecraft—Jeffreys, Sunderland, the judges, the Privy Council weighing this against that, opposing each other, agreeing, hesitating. Yet, in the end, it was his word and, to those who knew him well, it was clearly seen to be so because it carried the imprint of his honesty or (as most called it) his stupidity.

The Privy Council, before which the bishops were ordered to appear, met at five in the afternoon of Friday, June 8. When Sancroft and the others entered, James received them graciously enough and Jeffreys, as Lord Chancellor, handed the Archbishop the original Petition which Lloyd had presented on his behalf three Fridays ago.

'Is this the Petition that was written and signed by Your Grace and which these Bishops presented to His Majesty?' asked Jeffreys.

Sancroft ignored him and spoke directly to the King: 'Sir, I am called here as a criminal, which I never was before in my life and never thought I should be, especially before your Majesty. But, since it is my unhappiness to be so at this time, I hope your Majesty will not be offended if I am cautious in answering questions. No man is obliged to answer a question which may tend to the accusing of himself.'

The old man spoke it as if he had been briefed by counsel and learnt the speech by heart—as, in fact, he had. Once more James was taken off his guard by the unexpectedness of it.

'This is mere chicanery,' he said. 'Surely you don't deny your own handwriting?'

The archbishop refused to answer and Lloyd intervened smoothly with: 'All divines of all Christian churches agree that no man in our circumstances is obliged to answer such a question as has been put to us.'

'But I demand an answer,' said James.

'Then,' said Sancroft, 'though we are not obliged to give any answer, if your Majesty lays it upon us as a command, we shall give it, trusting to your Majesty's justice and generosity that we shall not suffer for our obedience if our answer should be brought in evidence against us.'

This was too much for James. 'I shall not make it a command,' he said. 'If you deny your own handwriting, what common ground is there on which we can even talk to one another?'

So, for hour after hour, the legal battle had continued. Three times the Seven were ordered to withdraw; three times they were brought back, after the council in their absence had sought a way out of the impasse. At last they acknowledged the paper.

'Is this your Petition?' asked James, when they came back for the fourth time.

'Pray, sir, give us leave to see it,' said Sancroft, 'and if, upon perusal, it appears to be the same——'

James gave it to him. It was passed from hand to hand. They nodded assent.

'Yes, sir. This is our Petition and these are our signatures.'

'Who were present at the writing of it?'

'All of us who have subscribed it,' said Lloyd.

'Were no other persons present?' James asked Sancroft.

Sancroft was silent, but Lloyd answered again: 'It is our great infelicity that we are here as criminals and your Majesty is so just and generous that you will not require us to accuse either ourselves or others.'

'Why did you come up to London?' said James to Lloyd.

'I received a request from the Archbishop that my advice and assistance were required on affairs of the Church.'

'What affairs were you consulted about?'

'The matter of the Petition.'

'What do you mean by the dispensing power being declared illegal by Parliament?'

'The words are so plain that we cannot use any plainer.'

'What want of prudence or honour is there in obeying the King?'

'What is against conscience is against prudence and against honour too—especially in persons of our character.'

'Why is it against your conscience?'

'Because our consciences oblige us, as far as we are able, to preserve our laws and religion according to the Reformation.'

'You mean that the dispensing power is contrary to law?'

'We refer ourselves to the Petition.'

'How could reading my Declaration make you parties to it?'

'We refer ourselves to the Petition.'

There was silence. Then suddenly James shot at Lloyd, looking straight in his eyes, the question: 'Did you arrange the printing of the Petition?'

The Bishop's momentary hesitation confirmed James's suspicion. 'If this is one of the articles against us,' said Lloyd, returning the stare unfalteringly, 'we desire to answer it in Court.'

If one stubbornness was partially overcome, another, equally unforeseen, obtruded itself. The Bishops refused to enter into recognizances to appear before the Court. Though, the evening before, Sancroft had announced that he was willing to do so—for it was a mere technicality—he had in the interim been persuaded by Lloyd to change his mind.

Now, when Jeffreys pointed out that the alternative was imprisonment, which no one, least of all the King, desired, it was Lloyd who spoke: 'This entering into a recognizance may be prejudicial to us; and therefore we hope your Majesty will not be offended at our declining it.'

'We have had the advice of the best counsel in Town,' echoed the Archbishop, 'and they have warned us it may be to our prejudice.'

'I assure you it will not be so,' said James, adding wearily: 'But you will believe anyone before you will believe me.'

Once more they were commanded to withdraw and for over an hour members of the Privy Council, going out to reason with them, endeavoured to shake their resolution. But, set on public martyrdom and conscious that by now all London would be waiting for their purposed pilgrimage, they remained adamant. At last James realized that he had no further choice and signed the warrant for the imprisonment they insisted on. So they made their triumphal journey to the Tower.

Clarendon, arriving at the Tower on the Sunday afternoon, went first to the room allotted to Lloyd, where he found him busily engaged in writing.

'Your chronology, my Lord, still occupies you?'

'We must not allow ourselves to be overborne by the chances and changes of this mortal life,' answered Lloyd with a wan smile. Though Clarendon was his friend and, during the last week, had been his host, Lloyd was too uncertain of his loyalty to let him know that he was putting the last touches to a pamphlet, on which he had been engaged for several weeks, suggesting that the newly-born Prince of Wales was no son of the King and Queen but a child who had been smuggled into the palace in a warming-pan to ensure the Papist succession to the Throne.

'I have just come from St James's,' said Clarendon, 'where I saw the Prince.'

'We were deafened by the Tower guns firing in honour of the birth,' said Lloyd. 'It is a happy day for His Majesty. You were there in the bedchamber?'

'No, it was ten o'clock. I was in church.'

'The King did not send for you?'

'No.'

'I should have thought he would,' said the Bishop softly, 'seeing that the boy's birth robs your niece of the throne. More particularly since the Princess Anne was also absent—and the Archbishop of Canterbury.'

'I could wish, indeed, that the Archbishop had been there; for the cause of his absence was worse than the absence itself. If only you would enter into recognizances, my Lord, I can assure you——'

'We have already decided to do so,' replied the Bishop. 'We made our decision this morning.'

He assumed—correctly—that Clarendon would not see the connection.

III

The Queen

THE little Italian clock by the Queen's bedside struck
three. Mary Beatrice stirred sleepily. It would soon
be dawn. Before she fell asleep she had half-decided
that were she awake she would have the curtains drawn so
that, on this morning at least, she might watch the world
lighting. The Countess of Sunderland, who was on duty as
Lady of the Bedchamber, had humoured her whim for the
Prince of Wales's first sunrise; but there was still three-
quarters of an hour till dawn and the room was so quiet that
she thought the Countess must have fallen asleep. There was
no need to wake her for half an hour. At peace with all the
world, suffused with a sense of well-being, the Queen
nestled back into the pillows watching the shadows and
playing her childhood's game of matching them with people.
At the corner of the ceiling she found James, if one allowed
a peculiar tilt to his nose and assumed a fuller wig than he
ever wore . . .

She wondered if he was asleep. Or, if awake, as happy as
she. The child had solved all problems. With the succession
safe, he could laugh at his enemies. As mother of the Prince,
she could at last forgive him his infidelities. She realized,

suddenly, that she no longer resented Berwick, and was glad of it. He was on their side, loyal to the Faith and to the Crown. With another of James's mistresses, Catherine Sedley and her children, it was a different matter. She was a dangerous influence. She was said to burlesque the priests and in such a manner that even James roared with laughter. No person and no occasion was safe from her unexpected and irreverent wit. But she was now in polite exile at Weybridge and, as far as Mary Beatrice knew, James never visited her. As far as she knew . . . Did a wife ever know? . . . As the thought obtruded itself, she recognized the beginnings of that misery of jealousy and frustration which had so often overwhelmed her during the fifteen years' marriage. Yet, even as it started, she realized it was no longer the same. Now, she was mother of the Prince . . .

He was a fine child and seemed healthy enough, they said. Sir Charles Scarborough and the other physicians agreed that this time no risks were to be taken. He was to be spoon-fed with a thin paste of oat and barley meal. No breast milk. That, they had decided, had led to the deaths of the earlier children. Now modern methods would be used. Lady Powys, in charge of the Prince, had allowed her surprise to be mistaken for a slight protest, but she could be relied on to obey the doctors, especially as Sir William Waldegrave, determined to press the point, had announced with emphasis that he would not give the Prince half an hour to live if he were suckled.

But the boy would live. Of that Mary Beatrice now felt certain. The terrors of that day two months ago when she so feared a miscarriage and death that she sent in panic to James

at Chatham to come back to her—that same day when the
Princess Anne did in fact miscarry and when they thought
the Queen Dowager was dying—were now hardly a
memory. Even the fear of eighteen hours ago, when it was
discovered that Dr Hugh Chamberlen was unaccountably
not in London and so could not deliver her, seemed foolish.
That famous and fashionable man-midwife could have done
no better than Judith Wilkes and James's gay present to her
of a purse of £500 'for a good breakfast' expressed everyone's gratitude.

The boy would live . . . Mary Beatrice had fulfilled the
task laid on her as a frightened, angry girl of fifteen, who had
never heard of the James, Duke of York, whom diplomacy
proposed as her husband. In any case she had determined
from early childhood to take the veil with the Sisters of the
Visitation in whose convent adjoining the palace she spent
so much time. No marriage proposals should deflect her from
that destiny. In her determination she had defied all the
diplomats and the plan was on the point of being abandoned
when the Pope himself intervened. It was an event without
precedent—that letter from the Sovereign Pontiff to a mere
child. She had kept it, treasured it still, knew it by heart:
'Considering the influence of your virtues, We easily
conceived a firm hope that an end might come to the
persecution still smouldering in that kingdom and that the
Faith, reinstated by you in a place of honour, might recover
the splendour and security of former days—an effect which
no exterior power could accomplish but which might
become due to the victory of your piety.'

Her obedience had been instant and complete. Like a new

Esther, trying to obtain relief for the persecuted fellow-members of her faith, she had come to a heretic land to marry James a widower, an ageing amorist, whose blood, compared with hers, was *parvenu*. His conversion was not long delayed. Now he was king, toleration, in spite of the Faction, would be accomplished. Already, for the first time for a hundred years, English Catholics could openly practise their religion and bring up their children in their own faith. This was not due in any way to her virtues—for, though she had tried to live a dutiful and pious life, she had no illusions about her popularity—but at least the continuance of their safety would be secured by her son ...

The clock chimed the first quarter. Suddenly she felt hungry. She would like some broth. She called the Countess of Sunderland softly, not wishing to wake her with a start. As there was no answer, she called more loudly. There was still no answer. An imperious shout brought a young chambermaid hurriedly from the anteroom.

'Your Majesty?'

'Where is the Countess of Sunderland? Where is my nurse? Who is here in attendance?'

'Only me, your Majesty.' The girl was terrified. 'Shall I fetch the Countess?'

'Certainly. Where is she? Why did she leave me?'

'You were sleeping so peacefully, your Majesty, that they thought——'

'A Queen is not left alone at such times, unless——' A panic thought intruded. 'Unless there is great reason for it. What has happened? The Prince! The Prince is well? There is nothing——'

The girl was crying, on her knees now by the bed.

'Tell me the truth, girl. I shall not forgive you if you lie to me.'

Between her sobs the chambermaid told her that by mistake or by carelessness a dose of syrup prescribed for the Prince had been repeated with the result that he had been taken so ill that they feared he was dying. But all the doctors were with him. All of them—Sir Charles Scarborough, Sir William Waldegrave and the others. Everything possible was being done. Lady Powys was sure it would be all right. The King himself had ordered that the Queen was not to be awakened. . . .

'The King is there?'

'No, Your Majesty.'

'Then where is he?'

'He went to the chapel, Your Majesty, to pray.'

'Mater misericordiae'—the Queen's lips moved in prayer though no sound came. . . . 'Eia ergo, advocata nostra, illos tuos misericordes oculos ad nos converte . . .'

James knew what he must do. His will was bent to it, in spite of the lacerated heart and the questioning mind, but still his lips would not form the words. None would hear but God and God knew without the assurance of sound, yet he was certain that he must actually say, there in the quiet of the chapel, words which freely offered the boy to God. As Abraham offered Isaac. Yet to ask that his Isaac should be spared to him would be to nullify the offering . . . 'The Lord gave and the Lord hath taken away. Blessed be the name of the Lord' . . . Now it had come, it was not like that.

In the numbness of his misery, he could not even pray. He was held up by the habit of prayer which had become second nature to him. For years he had observed rigidly a rule of life which made him rise every morning at seven, say his first prayers as soon as he was so far dressed as not to catch cold; then, when fully dressed—when the Levee was over and the chattering had ceased—retire alone into his oratory to make half an hour's meditation before Mass... This discipline served him now. His body, his mind, his will slipped into the external pattern as naturally as if he were a soldier taking his place for battle. It was only his heart which would not respond.

He began, almost mechanically, his usual thanksgiving. He gave thanks for the gift of life itself and for its preservation while he was still a boy when he escaped 'from the hands of those same rebels that murdered my father a few months before'; for its later preservation, as a man, in so many sieges, skirmishes and battles by land and sea. He gave thanks that he had been enabled to acquire in life some degree of patience and had endured exile and perpetual calumny in a spirit, far indeed from that of a perfect Christian, but at least with some understanding of how a Christian ought to endure it and with some attempt to achieve it. Above all he gave thanks that his eyes had been opened to the truth of the Catholic Faith and that he had been received into Christ's Church. For a few moments he gazed steadily at the Blessed Sacrament and then his lips started to frame whispered words: 'I am forced to own that I have, by my sins, justly deserved the afflictions which Thou hast been pleased to send me; but I pray too that Thou wilt increase my patience to balance my sufferings.'

Beneath the formal words was a cry for help so intense that momentarily it exhausted his spirit. There seemed no answer; only an empty void, into which danced the faces that reminded him of his besetting sin—the pale, intense face of Berwick's mother, Arabella Churchill; the laughing impudence of Catherine Sedley, mocking him even there at his 'Popish prayers.' One by one they came, memories, but half-remembered, of his youth; the lightly-discarded mistresses of his exiles; the tempting eyes still round him at Court to which, in desire at least, he had surrendered. It was as if the devil had sent them to intercept his remorse. Imperceptibly he abandoned any attempt at prayer and let his mind wander idly among the phantoms. Then, in the midst of his weakness, he suddenly perceived his weakness. His mind saved him when his emotion and his will were gone. He saw himself ironically, as Catherine Sedley might have seen him—an aged lecher, pharisaically muttering a formula of prayer while hugging his sin to his heart. Seen so, he became the laughing-stock of his own intellect. If as a soldier he had elaborated the most brilliant tactics but so failed to protect one weak point where the enemy would infallibly attack; if, as a sailor, he had set sail in a magnificently appointed ship which had a leak in it, he would deserve a mortal censure. How much the more so here. This small amiable vice would nullify all. Sharply he recollected himself and was at prayer again, quite simply a vile, weak sinner with no excuses. 'For touching my heart to repentance, I give thanks unto Thee, O Lord; and may it please Thee to continue me this grace, which I very humbly pray for, to inspire me every day with a new horror against my besetting sin, that I may not relapse into it.'

He rose from his knees comforted. He had made the offer and the resolution freely, with no thought of his son or his present terror; yet, on his side, he would keep it as a sacred bargain. If God were good enough to spare his son's life, he would regard the boy, until death, as the living pledge of his continence.

Mary Beatrice, hearing James's voice at the bedchamber door, said to the Countess of Sunderland: 'Admit His Majesty quickly.' But she did not look at James as he came towards her, for now he needed no reassurance from her. She smiled down at the Prince of Wales in her arms, quite recovered, contentedly sucking his thumb.

IV

William and Mary

WILLIAM, Prince of Orange, in his luxurious palace at the Hague, received the news of the birth of the Prince of Wales without any change of expression. Only when the bearer of the unwelcome news had withdrawn did he allow his face to mirror his fury and to shout, as if giving a command in battle, 'Now or Never.' Even at that crisis of anger, however, his lifetime's habit of caution constrained him to phrase it in Latin—'Aut nunc aut numquam'—so that the guard outside the door, even if he heard it, would not understand. He opened the door quickly. There was no sign of interest on the soldier's face. William gave curt orders that the Princess, his wife, be requested to come to his apartments.

She, too, must be made to see that the moment of decision could no longer be evaded. He had no doubt how she would choose; but she must be made to do it—to take her stand, freely and finally, with her husband or with her father; with William of Orange or with James of England. He went back into his room and, standing before James's portrait, sharpened his anger once more.

William, son of James's sister, husband of James's daughter, shared with his uncle-father-in-law one virtue and one passion. Neither knew the meaning of cowardice; both found in hard physical exercise, especially riding, a release for their spirits. In other things, the contrast between them—separated by a mere sixteen years—was complete. Even though each had the long face, the eagle's nose and the sensual mouth which marked them Stuart, their bodies distorted the focus. James, tall, regal, scrupulous of his appearance; William, small, unsteady on his legs, a hump on his right shoulder and his 'hollow and asthmatical stomach' making him hold himself so that he looked more hunchbacked than he really was; his long, dry, bony hands, always dirty and—as a contemporary noticed—'crooked and with alarmingly long nails, more like talons than hands.'

If both had a certain impassivity of expression, the causes were contrary. James's simplicity, his unworldly assumption of other people's honesty and his knowledge of his own were as perfectly expressed by it as William's subtlety, his cynical distrust of all men and his ceaseless scheming for his own advancement were concealed. What for James was an index, for William was a mask.

Though both were men of overmastering sexuality, it manifested itself in opposites—for James a procession of mistresses and twenty-one known children; for William innumerable homosexual lovers of whom the most enduring were his cousin Zuylestein; Bentinck, who, his own age, had been his page in boyhood; and Keppel, his present page, for whom he was in the throes of a passion which was at last to

estrange the others.* But whereas James—in the words of
one who was not well-disposed to him—though 'wandering
from one amour to another, yet had a real sense of sin and
was ashamed of it,' William had only a sense of secrecy. Nor
was the secret, however much he might deceive himself on
the matter, anything but an open one in his court where, as
an English resident wrote complainingly, 'none but pimps
and bawds must expect any tolerable usage.'

James had fought tenaciously to save Mary, his eldest
child, from William. When, in 1677, William had arrived in
England to arrange the marriage for political reasons—he
twenty-seven; she fifteen—James was not at first seriously
alarmed and speaking 'with great passion' he made it
generally known that the King his brother had promised
never to dispose of Mary's hand without his consent. But
when this was reported to the King, Charles laughed it away
with: 'It is true I gave my brother such a promise; but,
Godsfish! he *must* consent.'

Incredulous, James realized the King was in earnest. He
expostulated, argued, besought. Charles retorted with the
plea of political necessity and reminded James of his duty
to the Crown. James, as always, accepted that as his first
loyalty. To him it was not a matter of politics; it was an
emotion, grounded in personal circumstances, reaching back
into his boyhood. The last moments which he, at thirteen,
had been allowed to spend with his father, when Charles I
was a prisoner doomed to death, were an enduring memory.
Again and again the little King, with that stammering but

---

*When William gained the English throne, the three were made
respectively the Earls of Rochford, Portland and Albemarle.

emphatic voice of his, had said: 'James, above everything, you must be loyal and obedient to Charles who will be King when they have killed me. Never be tempted from your duty to him. Promise me.' And James the man had kept the promise that James the boy had made in tears. His careless, laughing elder brother (who had been safe in France at the time) had perhaps never quite understood to what he was appealing when he brought loyalty into the conversation. James would keep his promise to their father still, even though it meant sacrificing his daughter. But before it came to that, he was prepared to argue whether 'political necessity' in fact required it.

If, as Charles insisted, it was necessary to have Holland on England's side in the diplomatic struggle against France, it was also politic to postpone the marriage until the war at that moment in progress between France and Holland was over. For four days James argued this point of view and eventually persuaded his brother to it. He had gained a breathing-space at least. Before the war was over, many things might happen. But his success was short-lived. Almost immediately William destroyed it. Unless the marriage were decided on within two days, the Prince stormed, he would return at once to Holland, 'and before I go,' he told Charles's minister with a directness he could not have used to the King in person, 'the King must choose how we shall live hereafter. I am sure it must be either like the greatest friends —or the greatest enemies.'

The threat, with its incalculable international conse-quences, cowed Charles.

'He shall have his wife,' said the King to the bearer of the

message, 'and you shall go immediately and tell my brother
so.' That, at that moment, he could not himself face James
was his only recognition of the tragic nature of the decision.

James, when the message was delivered, merely remarked,
frozen and impassive: 'The King shall be obeyed and I should
be glad if all his subjects were as obedient as I,' and went to
St James's to tell his daughter her fate.

Mary burst into an agony of weeping but could say
nothing. The shock left her literally speechless and for half
an hour she fell from one paroxysm into another, while
her father tried uselessly to comfort her. Then, seeing that
nothing could be done, he called her lady-in-waiting, said
to her: 'The King thinks it fit to bestow my daughter upon
the Prince of Orange: I think it fit to let you know,' and left
them. Mary cried all that afternoon and the whole of the
following day.

William and Mary were married within a fortnight in a
bedroom of St James's. It was William's birthday November
4, and on the morrow the mobs celebrated Guy Fawkes day
as never before. The Protestant succession was safe.

That was eleven years ago and now the birth of the Prince
of Wales endangered that succession. If the boy lived, the
throne of England had, after all, eluded William's grasp. His
ceaseless plotting, his careful diplomacy, his military pressure;
the brilliant assessment of the changing needs of each new
situation, the bribery in the present and the corrupting
promises for the future—all would have been in vain.

For sixteen years, since his first visit to England in 1672
when he had organized a 'fifth column' there under one of
his spies, William had prepared the way for his eventual

power. He had overlooked nothing, even to the printing and distribution of pamphlets calculated to inflame the mobs against any policy of which he did not approve. Some were produced secretly in London, but more were written and printed under his own supervision at the Hague and smuggled across the Channel as 'parcels of fine goods,' 'linen,' tobacco' and other convenient misnomers. The skeleton of that early organization had never been broken and was now proving useful for pamphlets about the origin of the Prince of Wales and the martyr-like integrity of the Seven Bishops.

William's most important contact at the English Court was unquestionably the Earl of Sunderland, the Secretary of State, who so completely controlled James that no person and no letter could get to the King except through him. When, at the beginning of the reign, Monmouth had rebelled against James, Sunderland had withheld Monmouth's last appeal for mercy and request for an audience— both of which James would certainly granted—so that 'King' Monmouth, as William's rival in the Protestant interest, should die and the obloquy of his death be firmly fixed on James. In this case, it must be admitted, Sunderland was not actuated solely by desire to please William. He was afraid that Monmouth would reveal to James, in exchange for his life, detailed and incontrovertible evidence of Sunderland's own treachery. This was suspected, though as a rule Sunderland's personal fascination and charm could be counted on to blind the intellect even of those he had betrayed.

Cunning, supple, shameless, cold of heart and abject of spirit, Sunderland's superb looks and elegance yet made him the glass of fashion and the mould of form. His famous drawl—'Whaat maaters it who saarves His Majesty, so lang aas His Maajesty is saarved?'—echoed round the coffee-houses in the tones of innumerable imitators. Stories of his fantastic bouts of gambling, during which he would play bassett for £5,000 a night, made—as his wife complained—'the horridest noise in the world'; they also indicated his apparently exhaustless wealth, drawn partly from his patrimony, partly from his wife's great fortune and mostly from innumerable bribes. With no beliefs and no principles but a worship of money, he simulated a lively interest in Catholicism as the surest way to keep control of James. And he kept his own counsel by guarding against the two great betrayers of secrets. Indeed, if he dazzled his dupes into blindness, it was partly because they had not the wit to interpret this sign which was patent enough. 'He disliked women,' one recorded, 'and he hated wine.'

His wife was—so it was supposed—the mistress of his uncle. That uncle, Henry Sidney, a year his junior, was a bachelor and reputed the handsomest man in Europe. Sent by Charles II as Envoy to Holland, Sidney had contrived to captivate William of Orange. He was, indeed, said to be the only Englishman to win William's 'trust and fancy' and—as it was tactfully reported—became 'his close agent (to say no more).' He and William were constantly in each other's company and the affair became notorious when Charles wrote personally to William to ask that George Monck, the architect of the Restoration, might be honoured by being made general of the British forces in the Dutch service, and William's reply was immediately to give the post to Sidney.

The pretence that the Countess of Sunderland was Sidney's mistress was a master-stroke of diplomacy, for it enabled Sunderland through her to betray all James's secrets to William without anyone questioning her correspondence as anything but 'commerce de galanterie.'

Sidney, however, was at the moment in England. The Countess at court still communicated to him at his country house the plans and resolutions taken each day by James— with which her husband each evening provided her—and Sidney continued to send them to Holland. But now this doubled correspondence must, William decided, cease. In the last stage of the campaign, no risks must be taken. Sidney must come back to Holland. He could return with Zuylestein who, obviously, must be sent to bear official congratulations to James on the birth of the Prince of Wales. Everything would be safe in Zuylestein's hands . . . To make assurance doubly sure, Keppel could go with him . . .

William's brain was racing, his mind far in the future, when Mary entered.

'You sent for me, William.'

The submissive tones—though he had broken her to them through eleven years of calculated cruelty—irritated him. He did not, even with a nod, acknowledge her presence before he rapped out:

'The brat's a month early. Have you heard?'

'I've had a letter from Anne.'

She handed William her sister's emphatic, untidy letter. In silence he read: 'My dear sister can't imagine the concern and vexation I have been in that I should be so unfortunate to be out of town when the Queen was brought to bed, for I shall never now be satisfied whether the child be true or false. It may be it is our brother, but God only knows . . .'

He broke off to ask: 'Do you think it is your brother?'

'How should I know if Anne doesn't?' Mary parried.

'She has her opinion,' retorted William and continued reading aloud: ' "Everybody knows, by her own reckoning, that she should have gone a month longer. After all this 'tis possible it may be her child; but, where one believes it, a thousand do not. For my part, except they do give very plain demonstrations, which is almost impossible now, I shall ever be of the number of unbelievers." You see?'

'I see, yes. "It is almost impossible now." '

'What are you going to do?'

'What do you wish me to do, William?'

'Write to Anne an inquisition. As detailed as you can make it. Whether anyone felt the brat stirring in the Queen's belly—whether any woman, except her papist bitches, saw her face while she was in labour—how near your father was to her—but you will know these woman's questions better than I.'

'Yes, William.'

'Let me see the letter before you send it.'

'Of course. And what shall you do?'

'Send Zuylestein.'

'I mean—here.'

'What should I do here?'

'Are you having prayers said for—my brother?'

'I shall decide that later in Council. It might be unwise.'

'They are being said in my chapel, William.'

She turned and left him before he could answer and went back to the security of her apartments in the Binnenhof.

Mary, at twenty-six, could hardly remember the frightened, weeping girl who had once clung desperately to her father, beseeching him to countermand his order for marriage. Since then her heart and mind had suffered too much. Nothing she had dreaded had been unfulfilled. On her honeymoon voyage to Holland she had had to watch her husband make public overtures to one of her ladies-in-waiting. That tall 'squint-eyed dragon' Elizabeth Villiers, whose wit and eccentricity, combined with a man's outlook, a masculine stride and a total absence of feminine charm made her the obvious companion for one of William's sex, was still, in theory, his mistress. Mary did not cavil at the relationship, harmless in its sterility and even useful by reason of its conventional appearance, but she bitterly resented Elizabeth's power to influence William's decisions on matters of state and policy. Even the knowledge that she, and she alone, as next in succession to the throne of England, was the key to his plans of power could not quite restore her confidence when Elizabeth chose to break it.

So gradually Mary became what they made her. William, for the first six years of their marriage, kept her in virtual imprisonment in the Palace in the Wood, about a mile from the Hague. The house, built by the Orange family, millionaire connoisseurs in comfort, was surrounded by a primeval oak forest and the richest gardens in Europe; and here, except for occasional official appearances, she was forced to live in a seclusion which scandalized the civilized courts of the

Continent. 'Until now,' wrote the French Ambassador in the year she became twenty-one, 'the existence of the Princess of Orange had been regulated thus: From the time she rose in the morning till eight in the evening, she never left her chamber, except in the summer, when she was permitted to walk about once in seven or eight days. No one had liberty to enter her room, not even her lady-of-honour, nor her maids-of-honour, of which she has but four; but she has a troop of Dutch *filles de chambre*, of which a detachment every day mount guard on her and have orders never to leave her.'

Only when her health broke under the strain and her father wrote angrily to William to demand that she had proper treatment for her illness was the monotony broken. But it had done its work. Thereafter, however she might try to evade, she did not fight.

William's final test of his mastery was brilliantly conceived. If she was tired of seclusion, he would in her twenty-second year give her gaiety. He chose January 30, the anniversary of the execution of her grandfather, Charles I. From her earliest years, she had kept this day with the rest of her father's house, as a day of mourning, prayer and fasting. So, in her loneliness in Holland, she kept it still. But now, suddenly, William burst unexpectedly and unannounced into her apartments, looked at her mourning habit and started laughing.

'Take that hideous thing off,' he ordered.

'You have forgotten what day it is, William,' she said.

'On the contrary, I have remembered it. The "man of blood" was my grandfather too, but I rejoice in the justice

done on him. Put on your gayest dress. You are dining with
me—in public.'

'I am fasting.'

'We shall see. You have an hour.'

At dinner, the Court watched with amusement as Mary
was presented with all the successive dishes of the state
banquet and one by one dismissed them, eating nothing.

William said only: 'You will be hungry for the comedy.'
She looked at him incredulous.

'I have ordered them to play a special comedy for you at
the theatre,' he explained.

She could endure no more. In front of them all she burst
into tears and begged William to excuse her attendance. He
merely laughed: 'But I know how you love the theatre. Of
course you will go. And it would be wise not to close your
eyes and ears as you have your mouth. It insults my consideration for you. My faithful subjects would resent that.' Her
tears became uncontrollable, but they did not save her from
witnessing the comedy.

From that moment, Mary was broken, and William had
but one more conjugal task to perform—to deflect her hatred
from himself to her father. In this he was so helped by
circumstances that he could not strictly claim credit for it
except in so far as it was part of his grand political design.
The greater strategy included the less.

Even as a child Mary had admired her cousin Monmouth.
They had played and danced and acted together in the days
when both had been happy at the court of Charles II. Now,
when Monmouth came as a fugitive and her father's sworn
enemy to the Court of the Hague to plan with William an

assault on the Crown of England, she fell in love with him. William deliberately threw them together, urging Monmouth to visit her every evening to teach her the new dances, and the amazed Dutch court beheld their cloistered Princess dancing with Monmouth, walking with Monmouth, skating with Monmouth, acting with Monmouth, dining with Monmouth. The Ambassadors could make nothing of it. ' 'Tis not to be conceived,' wrote one, 'that the Prince of Orange could suffer all those airs of gallantry between the Princess and the Duke of Monmouth.' James, when it was reported to him in England, was incredulous. He wrote to warn her that Monmouth would try to wrest the English succession from her and her husband: 'Let the Prince flatter himself as he pleases, the Duke of Monmouth will do his part to have a push with him for his crown.' When no attention was paid to his warning, he dropped the matter in a final angry note to William: 'I could say more to you upon this subject, but am not encouraged to do it, since I have found that you have had too little consideration for things that I have said to you, which I thought of concern to our family, though you did not.'

William smiled that James could be such a fool. When the hour struck he served his Orange family well enough. Secretly encouraging and aiding Monmouth's rebellion, he officially wrote to James offering to come over to England in person to lead the Royal troops against the rebel; and, though his services were not accepted, he still (through his agent Sunderland's interception of Monmouth's last letter) made certain of Monmouth's death. Thus at a stroke, he removed a rival, impressed James with his loyalty and ensured that his wife should turn her hatred on her father for executing the one man who had lightened her misery with a momentary happiness.

Since Monmouth's death, nearly three years had gone by, and, in them, Mary had ceased to struggle. There was nothing to live for, and nothing more, it seemed, that life could do to her. She ate too much and sat too long at cards, so that now, in the middle twenties, her face which had once been accounted beautiful could boast three chins and her tall body was swollen to a great bulk so that on the occasions when her tiny husband insisted, for conventional reasons, on walking with her in public arm in arm, it was, from a distance, as if some Gargantuan governess was taking a child for an airing.

When news had arrived in Holland that her stepmother, Mary Beatrice, was pregnant, Mary, doomed to childlessness rejoiced for her. She had always been fond of Mary Beatrice who, sympathizing with her dislike of Orange, gaily called her 'My Lemon.' For herself, she hoped it would be a boy, so that she need never be Queen of England. She wanted no more change, no more problems. Towards her father, she had by now ceased to have any feelings whatever. Even the hatred was gone. He was King of England. He had the duties of his station. Fulfilling them, he had married her to William and killed Monmouth. According to her sister, Anne, who had always been his favourite daughter, he was now rushing to destruction. In their letters to each other they referred to him as 'Mansel,' lest others should open them. She even thought of him as 'Mansel.' Events in England had become like a play which she watched in rehearsal and in which she was occasionally asked to play a small part, which, somehow, was never that of James's daughter, William's wife or Anne's sister as an onlooker would understand these relationships. The act in progress was about a smuggled supposititious baby, which was almost as improbable and complicated as the dramas of Mr Dryden and his rivals which she had always delighted in.

The plot had no relationship with life. She knew perfectly well, merely because she knew James and Mary Beatrice, that the new Prince of Wales was her brother. But the part she had been given was, for the moment, the important one of cross-examiner, and she would show them all that she could play, if she chose, as well as anyone. She would show them, too, that she, who would never experience a lying-in, had not been unobservant of the process in others. She would even surprise Anne, who was expecting her third child. 'Whether the milk that, as is said, was in the Queen's breasts, was seen by many, or conducted in a mystery?' . . . 'If many observed the child's limbs being slender at first, and then appearing all of a sudden to be round and full?' . . . 'Is the Queen fond of it?' . . .

Page after page she wrote until she had found thirty-three questions. She had hoped to make it forty but towards the end her imagination flagged.

Nevertheless she had seldom had greater pleasure in obeying William.

C

V

The Thirtieth of June

THE King of England was not left uninformed of the Prince of Orange's intentions. For months, ever since the announcement of the Queen's pregnancy, James's cousin, Louis XIV of France, had warned him of them. A mere three days before the Prince of Wales was born, Paul Barillon, Louis's Ambassador in London, had delivered to James the latest information about the Dutch naval preparations for the invasion of England. The source of the information was the Comte d'Avaux, the French Ambassador at the Hague, a brilliant diplomat whom nothing escaped. Unfortunately, the English Ambassador there, an impecunious Irishman, Sir Ignatius White (who was always known by his more splendid title of the Marquis d'Albeville in the Roman Empire), had been bought by William. So, although the true situation was regularly expounded to James by Barillon, briefed by d'Avaux, it only reached him days after d'Albeville had reported a false one.

Apart from his natural reliance on his own Ambassador, James had other reasons for doubting the credibility of the French stories. In the first place, and overriding all, it quite simply passed the bounds of his belief that William and

Mary could be guilty of such an action. William's mobiliza-
tion—if it were a fact—was explicable as a step in his awaited
attack on France, which was contending with Holland for
the mastery of Europe; and, were this the case, it was
obviously in Louis's interests to grapple England firmly to
his own side. Sunderland was never tired of pointing out to
James that, assuming the French reports of Dutch activity
were justified, any other hypothesis was almost beyond the
edge of absurdity. And, at this moment above all, James's
trust in Sunderland was at its peak, for he knew that the
Earl was within a few days of making an open profession of
Catholicism. That, in the state of popular feeling, this would
mean a certain amount of obloquy had not deterred him.
'Whaat'—as he had said solemnly to James—'does it praafit
a maan to gain the whole waarld and lose his own soul?'

The King, however, had another reason for refusing to
listen to Louis which was altogether his own. He, as Admiral
of England, had been the maker of the Navy and he was not,
in any circumstances whatever, going to insult his sailors.
Even if the impossible were true and a Dutch invasion were
planned, he had still enough faith in his fleet to dispense with
allies. He would not belittle his men by accepting Louis's
offer of sixteen French ships. On that point he was adamant.

He did, however, order twenty of his own ships to the
Downs with orders to shadow the Dutch fleet should it put
out to sea. And he ordered his army to camp for its annual
manœuvres on Hounslow Heath.

Within twenty-four hours, the Faction had set it about
among the people that the army was to overawe London
and the navy to block the way of escape abroad when James

ordered his Papists, by way of thanksgiving for the Prince's birth, to cut all Protestant throats.

When, a week after his refusal, Zuylestein and Keppel arrived in England with William and Mary's official congratulations on the birth of the Prince, James was quite certain that he was right. The Family, at least, was compact against the Faction and the mob. But Louis instructed Barillon to tell the King that, despite his attitude, the French ships were being kept in readiness should he after all need them.

Zuylestein acquitted himself well not only in his open diplomatic mission to the Court but in his secret, and more important, contact with the leaders of the Faction. This was the easier because his conversations with Sidney needed no screen. It was natural enough that he should talk with an old friend; and Sidney was the link with Sunderland as well as with the conspirators in the North.

These revolved round the stormy figure of William Cavendish, Earl of Devonshire. During Charles II's reign Devonshire, who was now nearing fifty, had been a leader in every design to exclude James from the succession. When James, in spite of everything, succeeded his brother, Devonshire found himself banished from Court, not for his political views, but on account of his persistent brawling, during which the sight of bands of retainers wearing the Cavendish livery were beginning to remind London of the Verona of the Montagues and Capulets. It was not that anyone was surprised, since, in his youth he had provoked a memorable fracas at the opera in Paris and a few years later had been imprisoned in London for his propensity for instigating duels. James, however, when he became King decided to rid the capital of at least that nuisance, and Devonshire had been fined £30,000 and sentenced to a term of imprisonment. He had at once retired to his seat at Hardwick in the almost inaccessible Peak District, had dared the Sheriff to arrest him and, to demonstrate to the world how little £30,000* meant to him, had started to build himself a palace in the Palladian style at Chatsworth.

His enforced absence from London had the advantage of forming a convenient cover for meeting other dissatisfied noblemen, including Danby, the architect of the marriage of William and Mary, whose vast estates in Yorkshire made him the other power in the North. About ten miles from Hardwick was a small inn, The Cock and Magpie, on the edge of Whittington Moor. Here secretly Devonshire met Danby, Shrewsbury, Lumley and Russell to discuss their plans for the support of William's invasion. These nobles, representing the wealth and power of England, considered themselves with reason as guarantors William could trust. For William had let it be known that he would not move until he had something more than vague promises of general goodwill. He must have a definite invitation and under-taking of support actually signed by the eminent and powerful. There need only be a few signatures—it would have been unrealistic to insist on many in a matter involving high treason—but they must be representative of great interests. And this the five could claim to be. In addition, all were menaced by James's policy which, they believed, would

---

* In the currency of the time. The equivalent would be about £150,000 in Victorian values and an incalculable sum today.

have eventually returned their wealth and property to the Church from which it had originally been stolen. They were equally threatened by James's intention to allow Catholics to hold positions of power and responsibility in the State, since such competition would both destroy their monopoly and reveal their mediocrity.

Zulyestein, assessing the weight of the five peers, decided that his master would accept their guarantee; but, through Sidney, he pointed out that there must also be some representative of the Lords Spiritual, since the Calvinistic William was coming over as the avowed champion of the Church of England.

Fortunately, the selection of a bishop to add to the number presented no difficulty. The claims and co-operation of Henry Compton, Bishop of London, were, if anything, too obvious. As brother of the Earl of Northampton, he was in his temporal interests already one with them; and, ecclesiastically, James had no bitterer enemy.

Compton, as a younger son, had been intended for the army, but discovering that he disliked the dangers inseparable from warfare, had decided at the age of twenty-nine to change careers and enter the Church. After a year's theological study, in which he contrived to learn singularly little about the faith he was supposed to teach, he was ordained. His rapid preferment was a matter of course. By way of wealthy sinecures and canonries, he had reached the episcopal bench as Bishop of Oxford and at the age of forty-two had been translated to London on his way—so he, in common with everyone else, assumed—to the Archbishopric of Canterbury. Then, between him and his hopes had stepped

James, who informed his brother, King Charles, that it would be a scandal of the first magnitude to give the Archbishopric to Compton, who had a deserted wife (belonging to his soldiering days) still alive.

So it was that Sancroft had become Primate of All England and Compton, in London, had been left to revenge himself as best he could. He had as it happened been able to wound his enemy to the quick. When Mary was fourteen and Anne eleven, he had gone to James and suggested that it was now time that Mary, at least, should be confirmed so that she could receive Communion according to the rites of the Church of England.

James replied: 'As you know, my Lord Bishop, I am prohibited by my Faith to participate in any Anglican rites; and, for the same reason, I cannot allow my daughter to.'

'But as it is both the Lady Mary and the Lady Anne attend the services of the Church of England,' answered Compton.

'That is, as you know, for reasons of state and against my will as their father.'

'But they have not been instructed in your own religion.'

'And you, my Lord Bishop, know perfectly well why. If I had made the least move to have them brought up in what I consider the true Faith, they would have been taken away from me altogether and I should have been left a father without a family. Indeed, I doubt whether I should have been permitted to see them at all except on public state occasions.'

'Then may I put it to Your Royal Highness that as you observed the laws of the state in not instructing them in the doctrines of the Church of Rome, so you will allow me to observe the same laws by instructing them in the beliefs of the Church of England?'

'I will not give my consent,' said James, and went out of the room.

Next day, Compton had returned to the attack and suggested that the matter should be laid before the King. James, bowing to the inevitable, agreed. Charles, who as King could do nothing else, had ordered Compton immediately to instruct the two Princesses in the tenets of the Established Church and to confirm the elder.

'His Majesty has ordered it,' the Bishop reported to James, not concealing his glee.

'So I expected,' said James. 'But that means that what you do, you do by the King's command; neither on your own authority nor with my consent.'

Compton had made the most of his opportunity. At every instruction, he was careful to leave on the impressionable minds of the two girls a conviction of the foolishness, if not the actual wickedness, of their father's Faith. And the last bitter drop in James's cup on that evening of mockery when Mary was married to William in her bedchamber at St James's had been that Compton had performed the ceremony.

James, when he became King, realized that it was his duty to Anglicans and Catholics alike to set up a body, composed entirely of Anglicans, to enforce discipline in the Church of England, lest any official interference on his part should be resented and consequently abuses in the Establishment would flourish without reproof. He therefore instituted the Ecclesiastical Commission, over which the Archbishop of

Canterbury presided, assisted by two Bishops, the Lord
Chancellor, the Lord High Treasurer, the Secretary of State
and the Chief Justice of the Common Pleas. It had been
unfortunate that the first case to come before the Commission
was that of Compton, who had secretly inspired and openly
allowed the Rector of St Giles-in-the-Fields to preach
sermons which were politically seditious and personally
insulting to the King. When Compton as Bishop of London
was ordered to suspend the Rector, he had refused and, after
a trial, had himself been suspended and required 'to abstain
from the function and execution of his episcopal office.'

So he retired to his palace at Fulham and devoted himself
to the one subject in which he was learned—botany. He
collected, mostly from friends or travellers in America, a
greater variety of exotic plants and trees than had been seen
anywhere before in England. But this indulgence of his
amiable passion did not prevent him continuing to intrigue
against James, chiefly through the Princess Anne, over whose
weak and sentimental mind he had, from her childhood,
exercised an iron ascendancy. And, though he was precluded
from sharing the public stage with the Seven Bishops, he
gave them what private advice and encouragement lay in
his power. Consequently, as soon as he was invited by
Henry Sidney to join with Devonshire and Danby and
Shrewsbury and Lumley and Russell and Sidney himself in
providing the country with another 'Immortal Seven' who
should send an official invitation to William of Orange, he
assented with alacrity. He was additionally delighted that, by
paying a visit to the Peak District at that month, when the
trial of the Seven Bishops was about to take place in

London, he would incidentally offer a public proof of his innocence in their intrigue.

The jury for the trial was picked with some care. All, by necessity, were Protestants, and some Nonconformists were given places as likely to be more hostile than even the Anglicans to the King's faith. The foreman was a wealthy baronet and most of his colleagues were men of great possessions. The only doubtful voice was that of Michael Arnold, brewer to the palace, who ingenuously announced his impartiality before the proceedings started: 'Whatever I do, I shall be half-ruined. If I say "Not Guilty!" I shall brew no more for the King, and if I say "Guilty!" I shall brew no more for anyone else.'

The Attorney-General, Sir Thomas Powis, a third-rate lawyer who led for the Crown, had against him the most brilliant practitioners at the Bar, including two former Judges, two former Law Officers and a former Recorder of London, as well as a junior whose dazzling gifts were soon to lead him to the Woolsack. The wealth of the Faction had, by briefing them, ensured such a disparity of talent as had never been known in English legal history. And to make the verdict trebly sure, 'public opinion,' which had been inflamed to fever heat during the three weeks between the Bishops' triumphal journey to the Tower and their trial in Westminster Hall, was not left unrepresented. As an eye-witness noted, 'at the great trial were between thirty and forty Lords, which indeed frightened the judges and jury, for they fancied that every one brought a halter in his pocket.'

The technical charge against the Bishops was that they had

written and published in the County of Middlesex a false,
malicious and seditious libel—that Declaration in which not
only had they made it public that they considered it impossible 'in prudence, honour or conscience' to obey the
King by reading his edict of religious toleration but had also
enunciated the opinion that the Royal Prerogative was
subject to Parliamentary control. The facts of the case were
indeed such that it never occurred to James—or, for that
matter, to anyone who had impartially examined them—
that any verdict but 'Guilty' was possible. The Bishops'
lawyers above all realized that their only defence lay in a
technicality.

The proceedings therefore opened with a repetition of the
long wrangle which the Bishops had already had with James
on the subject of handwriting. After some hours, the
Attorney-General reluctantly put the Clerk of the Privy
Council in the box to swear that he had overheard the
Bishops acknowledge their signatures to the King. That
elementary point at last being established—that the writing
was Sancroft's—the defence then fell back on the line that
as Sancroft had been ill and had not accompanied the other
six when the petition was delivered, there was no evidence
that it had been written in Middlesex. Lambeth, being south
of the river, was in Surrey. Nor could there be any proof
that that petition, written in Surrey, was the same one that
was handed to the King at Whitehall, in Middlesex. The
defence did not deny, of course, that the handing of the
petition to the King did, in fact, legally constitute 'publication' in Middlesex. But, since no one was present at the
interview except the King and the Bishops and the King, by

law, could not and the Bishops, by choice, would not testify on the subject, no proof could be offered.

Once again the Attorney-General was forced into a course which he would have preferred to avoid. Sunderland, now at the peak of his unpopularity because of his conversion to Catholicism, had to be sent for. As his sedan-chair made its way through Westminster Hall, there were shouts of 'Popish dog!' He was noticed to be pale and uncertain as he gave his evidence. Even his drawl was modified as he told the court that the Bishops before they were admitted into the Royal presence had informed him of their intention to petition the King, and as, after they had left, the King had in his hands a petition signed by them, it might reasonably be inferred to the satisfaction of any jury that the two were the same.

The defence, being at last driven to the point of defending the actual petition as being neither false nor malicious nor seditious, fell back on the arguments of the Parliamentary lawyers in their struggle against the Crown in the earlier years of the century. Only by ignoring the Restoration settlement and assuming the complete dependence of the King on Parliament could they question the Crown's right to dispense certain laws by the direct exercise of the Royal Prerogative. This was revealed as the vital question. The Bishops had, indeed, as James had accused them of doing, raised the standard of revolt—a revolt against the concept of monarchy itself. One of the judges actually put it into words. He declared that there could be no libel since the Declaration of Indulgence was itself a nullity and that, if the King were allowed such power, there would be an end of Parliaments.

'That issue, gentlemen,' he concluded, 'I leave to God and your consciences.'

The only juror whose conscience was seriously troubled was Michael Arnold the brewer. Though all the others found for the Bishops, he held out. Impatiently, Thomas Austin, a country gentleman of vast estates, offered to argue the question point by point with him.

'No,' said Arnold, 'I've not the brain to reason and debate; it's my conscience that's not satisfied. I shall not acquit the Bishops.'

'Look at me,' said Austin. 'I'm the largest and strongest of you here; but before I find their petition a libel, I'll stay here till I'm no bigger than a tobacco pipe. That's *my* conscience.'

All through the stifling June night, Arnold held out. The jury were guarded in their room by the Bishops' solicitors, who with a troop of servants sat on the stairs leading to it to see that the officials on the door passed no food within. About four in the morning, some basins of water for washing were allowed to be taken in. The jurymen, raging with thirst, drank it all. Arnold, almost fainting with physical discomfort and the unrelenting attacks of eleven men whom he knew to be his intellectual superiors, endured for two hours more. At six o'clock he capitulated. The jury was unanimous for the acquittal of the Bishops.

When the verdict was officially given in Westminster Hall a little past ten o'clock on that morning of Saturday, June 30, London went mad. The spectators in the Hall itself, who numbered about ten thousand, raised a cheer that, as Clarendon recorded it in his diary, 'one would have thought the hall had cracked.' The waiting thousands outside answered with another shout and the third hurrah was heard clearly at Temple Bar. The innumerable boats on the Thames took up the cry and the larger ones fired salvoes of gunpowder. For half an hour the noise was so continuously deafening that conversation was impossible. Then a new sound added itself to the tumult. As if answering to a single signal, all the church bells of Westminster and the City started ringing peals of victory.

The Bishops took refuge from an enthusiasm which, welcome as it was, might have become too exhausting by visiting the nearest chapel; the jurymen emerged from the Hall limp with a thousand handshakes; and the nobles who had proved such valuable spectators added the final touch of joy to the occasion as they drove slowly away in their coaches by throwing handfuls of money to the crowd for the drinking of the Bishops' healths.

James was not in London that morning. He was among his soldiers on Hounslow Heath. At ease there among the simplicities of loyalty, he had shown a special mark of honour to the newly-appointed Lieutenant-General, Lord Churchill, whom he trusted above all men, by dining on the first day in his tent.

He had known John Churchill for twenty-three years since, as a boy of fifteen, he had become his page. In his twenties, Churchill had gone to the wars where he had made himself so great a reputation as a soldier that the great Turenne himself had complimented him. After his return he had been inseparable from James and had accompanied

him on both his exiles. When James was in Scotland, he
served him as confidential emissary to King Charles in
England and was rewarded by a Scots peerage and the
command of the only regiment of dragoons then in existence.
This was generally regarded as a flagrant piece of favouritism
on James's part and the ballad-mongers lampooned it:

> Let's cut our meat with spoons:
> The sense is as good
> As that Churchill should
> Be put to command the dragoons.

But James, there at least, was not mistaken in his estimate of
one who was to prove one of the greatest soldiers in history.
When James came to the throne, Churchill was given an
English peerage, was made major-general and colonel of
the 3rd Horse Guards and showed both his ability and his
loyalty in the crushing of Monmouth's rebellion.

The ties between the two were drawn even closer by the
circumstances which had first introduced Churchill to James's
service—James's love for John's elder sister, Arabella, who
became the mother of Berwick and three other of his
children. It was in the year of the Great Plague, 1665, that
James had fallen in love with her. She was then a lanky,
awkward, seventeen-year-old Maid of Honour to his wife;
he, at thirty-one, was the hero of England who, as Lord
High Admiral, had just won a spectacular sea victory over
the powerful Dutch fleet. His brother Charles had sent him
to York to take command in case of a threatened rebellion
in the north, and during his seven weeks of inactivity there
he had relieved the tedium by indulging continuously in his

favourite outdoor sports. As an incidental diversion he had
tried to teach his wife's maids-of-honour to ride properly.
Arabella was a disappointingly inapt pupil and when one
day, at a coursing match, James had noticed her sitting her
horse badly, he had ridden over to reproach her for so
disgracing her tutor.

The sequel had been sufficiently memorable for the incident
to be recorded by a French eye-witness and, published in
his memoirs, to delight the gossips of Europe. Arabella's
embarrassment at James's reproof 'had added to her natural
paleness: in this situation her countenance had almost com-
pleted the Duke's disgust, when her horse, desirous of
keeping pace with the others, set off at full gallop, in spite of
all her efforts to prevent him; and, her endeavours to hold
him in firing his mettle, he at length set off at full speed, as if
he was running a race against the Duke's horse. Miss
Churchill lost her seat, screamed out and fell from her horse.
A fall, while the horse was going at so quick a pace, must
have been violent and yet it proved favourable to her in every
respect; for without receiving any hurt, she gave the lie to
all the unfavourable suppositions that had been formed of
her person in judging from her face. The Duke alighted in
order to help her. She was so greatly stunned that her
thoughts were otherwise employed than about decency on
the present occasion; and those who first crowded round her
found her in rather a negligent posture. They could hardly
believe that limbs of such exquisite beauty could belong to
Miss Churchill's face. After this accident, it was noticed that
the Duke's tenderness and affection for her increased every
day.'

If John Churchill owed his introduction to Court to his sister's love-affair, he equally owed the foundation of his pecuniary fortune to an even stranger one of his own. The eyes of one of King Charles's mistresses, the insatiable Lady Castlemaine (who was already keeping two other lovers), lighted on the handsome face, the winning manner and the soldierly form of young John Churchill, then an ensign in the Foot Guards. He not only made no objections to her proposals but boasted openly of his good fortune. Even in that scandalous court, his advertisement, if not his complaisance, was felt to be beyond the bounds of the permitted and Charles was informed of the matter by one of his courtiers, who even insisted on accompanying him to the Castlemaine's room at a moment when Churchill was known to be in it. But the young man saved the situation by jumping out of the high window just before the King entered—a feat for which the grateful Castlemaine presented him with five thousand pounds, which, with his natural prudence, he immediately invested in an annuity.

Churchill's devotion to money was indeed his ruling passion. He made no secret of it and such was the single-mindedness of his worship that, years later, when he had amassed the largest private fortune in Europe, he actually refused to lend the aged Castlemaine a small sum to pay a gambling debt—a circumstance commemorated by the poet Pope:

> The gallant, too, to whom she paid it down
> Lived to refuse his mistress half a crown.

But James, though he was aware of Churchill's avarice,

did not distrust it. It never occurred to him that if the
man had so markedly one of the characteristics of Judas, he
might conceivably have the other. He was always completely at ease in Churchill's company and, as he chatted
with him and Feversham, the Commander-in-Chief, on
that June morning on Hounslow Heath, his spirits revived
sufficiently to make him almost forget the trial proceeding
in London.

That same thirtieth of June, far away in the Peak, the
other 'Seven' were holding their decisive meeting. They
were an oddly assorted gathering. The Earl of Danby, the
eldest of them—he was nearly sixty—appeared more a
skeleton than a man as he sidled up to the florid, bulky
Devonshire. The two youngest, the Earl of Shrewsbury and
Lord Lumley, both in their twenties, were hereditary
Catholics who had recently turned Protestant and though
they were united by hatred of the fervour with which the
King was defending the faith they had abandoned, they had
little else in common. The head of the ancient family of
Talbot, Shrewsbury, who was comprehensibly nicknamed
'King of Hearts,' despised Lumley's Irish blood and deplored
his manners. Russell and Sidney, too, had a common bond
in that both had been in James's Household and both had
spent many years with William at the Hague plotting their
master's ruin, but apart from this similarity of experience,
the contrast between the bitter, bronzed sailor and the bland,
soft courtier was complete.

Compton, the newcomer, stood somewhat isolated from
the rest. He had for safety abandoned his episcopal clothes

and was dressed in his favourite disguise as a soldier. In this
way he had excited no suspicion on his journey, since in any
case, as his clergy had noticed, he was accustomed to talk
more like a colonel than a bishop. He found it now a pleasant
coincidence that he was able to intervene decisively in a
discussion on the military situation. . . . When William
landed and attacked from the south, Devonshire and Danby,
who counted on being able to raise the North for William
without difficulty, would create a diversion. But where
was best to strike? Where was James likely to muster his
army? . . .

'It does not matter greatly,' said Compton, 'for Churchill
will lead the army over to us.'

'*Churchill?*' Devonshire and Shrewsbury were both
incredulous.

'Certainly,' said the Bishop smoothly, 'but he will, of
course, give no sign till the last moment.'

'But what proof have you of this?' asked Danby.

'I have no actual proof,' replied Compton, 'but your
Lordships will understand that my visits to the Princess
Anne, who, I am pleased to say, shows every day more
devotion to the Church of England than she did even as a
girl—that my frequent visits to the Cockpit enable me to
understand very well what is intended. Need I say more?'

There was no need. They understood perfectly. The
Princess Anne's London residence, the Cockpit, was the
centre of the intrigue in London. Anne herself was completely
in the power of Churchill's wife, Sarah, her Lady-in-Waiting,
who dominated her at every point where Compton's own
influence terminated. The jest that Anne was a model wife

and daughter—Lady Churchill being the husband and the Bishop of London the father—had the sting of truth.

'If we can rely on Churchill,' said Sidney, 'there need be no bloodshed; but I for one would not count on it. In any case, it is a matter we can discuss nearer the time. What is urgent is this paper. I have written it out for your signatures. Let me read it to you.'

They all listened attentively as Sidney's mellow voice read the document assuring William that nineteen-twentieths of the English people were desirous of a change and would willingly join to effect it, if only they could obtain the help of such a force from abroad as might secure those who should rise in arms from the danger of being dispersed and slaughtered before they could form themselves into anything like military order. If His Highness would appear in England at the head of some troops, tens of thousands would hasten to his standard. He would soon find himself at the head of a force greatly superior to the whole of the King's army. It was important to take some decisive step before the King had remodelled the army. The Prince should come with as little delay as possible. They, the signatories, pledged their honour that they would join him and they undertook to secure the co-operation of as many persons as could safely be entrusted with so dangerous a secret. On one point, however, they thought it their duty to remonstrate with His Highness. He had sent congratulations to Whitehall and had thus seemed to acknowledge the child who was called the Prince of Wales as the rightful heir to the throne. This was a grave error and had damped the seal of many. Not one person in a thousand doubted that the boy was supposititious;

and the Prince would be wanting to his own interests if the suspicious circumstances which had attended the Queen's confinement were not put prominently forward among his reasons for taking arms.

After they had all signed, Herbert, a discontented sailor, had been deputed to take the precious paper secretly to Holland; and Shrewsbury won much commendation by declaring that he would shortly follow and take £12,000 of his own fortune to help William finance the invasion.

The express messenger whom Sunderland had dispatched to Hounslow with the news of the acquittal of the Bishops was at once admitted to the King's presence. As he gave his message, James could not control his look of surprise and annoyance or check a muttered: 'So much the worse!' But his voice was steady as he acknowledged the news. The man had hardly left when, from the confines of the camp, came the sound of cheering. James asked Feversham to ascertain the cause of it, though he had more than half guessed it. During his visit it had not escaped his notice that there was considerable tension between the Catholics and the Protestants among the troops, and, if the news of the acquittal had been spread in the camp, it was not impossible that the one would cheer in order to taunt the other. He hoped, however, that discipline would have prevented it.

Feversham, returning, dispelled the hope.

'What is it, my Lord?'

'Nothing, your Majesty; merely some of the soldiers applauding the verdict.'

'Do you call that nothing?' said James curtly, and gave

immediate instructions to his entourage to prepare to return to London.

On the ride back, he turned over the circumstances of the trial in his mind and gradually he began to see that he had made a major political blunder. He should have listened to those advisers who had urged him in the first place not to prosecute the Bishops and then, when the Prince of Wales was born, at least to seize the occasion as an excuse to grant them a free pardon. Instead, he had sided with the opposite party in the Council led by Sunderland, who were for severe measures. Had, he wondered, all his advisers been honest in their advice? Was it possible that he was being urged towards a precipice while a veil of loyalty and concern for his welfare was being used to blindfold him? But as his rigid daily self-examinations had accustomed him to accuse himself before he accused others, he put aside such suspicions and turned to himself. It was clear that he had made a mistake; but how had he made it? Pared down to essentials, the present crisis had revealed that, at all costs, the leaders of the Church of England would resist toleration and considered even an incitement to rebellion a permissible means to thwart that end. Why? Then he suddenly saw that—as he put it later—'he had sought to deprive them of the one privilege which was nearer their heart than he had imagined; he had tried to wrest the sword of persecution out of their hands. They could not enjoy peace if others had it also, nor could they bear to be put on an equality with those who for so long had stood in awe of their authority.' He had thought they would act as Christians and, in his simplicity, had forgotten that they were public men belonging to a wealthy and privileged caste. It was a major blunder and he would have to call up all the statesmanship he possessed to repair it. He was satisfied that he could do it without compromising his faith, for it was Father Petre, the Jesuit on the Privy Council, who had, in the first place, opposed the prosecution of the Bishops. It was not too late for all to be remedied.

But that night in London he almost despaired. Never within living memory had there been such a glare of bonfires, round which the mob danced in drunken glee, toasting the damnation of the Papists. The noise of rockets, squibs and firearms was incessant. And outside his own apartments in Whitehall was the largest bonfire of all, at which an effigy of the Pope was solemnly committed to the flames. The great wax figure had been moulded with care. It wore a chasuble, and on its head was the tiara. Inside the wicker frame which was its body was a large sack, in which had been sewn up a quantity of live cats, so that their screams and the smell of their burning flesh should lend verisimilitude to the rite.

With almost miraculous self-control James, watching from the window, refrained from ordering his guards to go out and end the obscenity. Instead, he went to his oratory. He was in tears.

VI

High Summer

WILLIAM did not wait for the arrival of the Invitation to push forward his preparations and when Russell and Shrewsbury arrived in Holland they found it a scene of warlike activity. Twenty-four new men-of-war were being built and fitted out and six thousand sailors had been added to the naval establishment. The gunmakers of Utrecht and the saddlers of Amsterdam were working overtime; from all over the country, field-pieces and ammunition were pouring into a central camp; seven thousand recruits were being drilled as a reserve and tens of thousands of seasoned soldiers were assembling near the coast. The Prince was spending freely the £250,000 which, over the past years, he had been hoarding for the emergency and was now awaiting the 100,000 guineas which was being subscribed by the Faction in England, though some of that would have to return to the country in the form of bribes and upkeep of his propaganda organization there. He accepted with great pleasure Shrewsbury's personal gift and assured him of a Dukedom, after the Invitation had been suitably answered.

Russell immediately set to work to organize a special and

secret express service to England, and before the month was
out a boat whose lightness gave it a record speed ran regularly
between Schevening and a deserted creek in East Anglia,
under the command of Danby's son and heir, Lord
Dunblaine.

During those early July days, Mary saw very little of
William. He was always either in council or looking at his
new ships (which, as he had explained to her, were to deal
with the menace of the Algerian pirates) or his army (which
might be needed for defence against a sudden and un-
provoked aggression by Louis of France). On the few
occasions when they met, she noticed that he was more
taciturn than usual. Once he had assured her solemnly:
'Never in my life did I so much feel the need of God's
guidance,' but usually his topic of conversation was Anne's
letters about the Prince of Wales.

Anne's answer to the long list of questions Mary had sent
was not altogether satisfactory. Fact was so mixed with
speculation that it was difficult to form an accurate picture.
Nor had Anne quite grasped the point of her query about
the child's limbs being slender at first and then all of a
sudden to be round and full—which would establish it as a
changeling.

'I never heard what you say of the child's limbs,' her sister
wrote. 'As for seeing it dressed or undressed, they avoid it as
much as they can. By all I have seen and heard, sometimes
they refuse almost everybody to see it; and that is when they
say it is not well; and there is always a mystery in it, for one
does not know whether it is really sick and they fear one
should know it, or whether it is well and they want one to

think it is sick, as her other children used to be. In short, it is not very clear anything they do; and, for the servants, from the highest to the lowest, they are all Papists.'

There was really very little to go on, too, in the answer to: 'Is the Queen fond of it?'—'I dined there the other day when they said it had been very ill of a looseness, and it really looked so; yet when she came from prayers she went to dinner without seeing it, and after that played at Comet and did not go to it till she was put out of the pool.' The Queen might, reflected Mary, have played cards to keep her mind off a situation which she could do nothing to improve. That would have been natural enough. She had done it too often herself not to understand it.

The only positive news was in Anne's letter of July 9 when she reported gleefully: 'The Prince of Wales has been ill these three or four days; and if he is as bad as some people say, I believe it will not be long before he is an Angel in Heaven.'

Mary could not understand why, when she showed this to William, he was so angry.

The Prince of Wales had indeed been ill. The diet of barley-flour, water and sugar which the doctors had pre-scribed in place of milk was not successful and the remedies used when the baby showed symptoms of its ill-treatment made matters worse. The Tuscan Ambassador, who had been permitted to see the child, was sufficiently scandalized to write home to his master: 'The quantity and quality of the stuff they pour into that tiny body is incredible. There are more than thirty bottles on the table of his room, among

them canary wine, which they have given him to drink, and
drops known as Dr Goddard's. These are nothing less than
liquid fire, for if one falls on a woollen cloth, in half an hour
it burns a hole. The drops consist of sal ammoniac, dried
viper and "the skull of a person hanged." '

James and Mary Beatrice continued to suggest to the
doctors that perhaps, after all, mother's milk would be a
better diet for their son; but the specialists, however they
might disagree on the best remedy, were still unanimous
that, were he given milk, he would be dead in half an hour.
Neither parent dared take the risk of defying the doctors, but
Mary Beatrice, looking at the pale little face beneath the
cooling head-bandages, determined to call the saints to her
aid and a special courier was dispatched to beg a particle of
the relics of St Achatius, the martyred Roman soldier who
had been tortured with a crown of thorns.

The intense heat of a pitiless July and an outbreak of
smallpox made the situation worse and the King insisted on
at least taking the precaution that none but the Household
should have access to the Prince and that apartments for him
should be prepared immediately in the better air of Richmond Palace.

Yet the child, in spite of the doctors, made a temporary
recovery and his parents were able, without that anxiety, to
appear at the great firework display on the Thames which had
been staged to celebrate his birth and his mother's reappear-
ance in public after her month's seclusion. It was the last
official function before the Court left London for the summer
recess. Zuylestein had remained in England, ostensibly to
attend it and congratulate the Queen in person. He was, for

the occasion, the guest of Clarendon who, since his house did not overlook the river, had joined the Duchess of Richmond's party. The performance, which was impressive enough, lasted four hours. The thousands of balloons released to fall gracefully on the water as the light faded; the twelve gigantic rockets, bursting into fantastic shapes to lighten the dark; the great set-piece of Bacchus as Plenty, astride a great tun which suddenly discharged nine barrels of fireworks of every kind, and the lesser, but still enormous, female figures representing Fecundity and Loyalty, with their emblems of a hare and a hen with chickens—all these drew plaudits from the spectators. Yet they were overtopped by a circumstance which none could have foreseen. From first to last, summer lightning streaked the sky and eclipsed in its brightness all the ingenuity of man.

Zuylestein, watching it, speculated on the use to which his spreaders of rumour would put it on the morrow. Obviously it could be interpreted as a sign of God's displeasure, though such an interpretation had the drawback that it could equally well be counter-construed as a signal of Divine co-operation. . . . He was not, of course, officially concerned with such humble members of the Orange organization as the pamphleteers and the spreaders of rumours; his interest was personal, springing from a cynicism which saw no limits to human credulity. He was particularly amused by a new recruit, one Honeyman, a butcher in Newgate, who had been encouraged to give full rein to his professional fantasies, with the consequence that, at the moment, it was firmly believed that the King's chapel at St James's was filled with large cauldrons for boiling heretics in;

large gridirons; several large spits to hold seven or eight
heretics to be roasted at once, and strangely shaped knives
for cutting throats. There were also 'Protestant Bridles.'
These would serve for leading heretics about the streets of
London and Westminster until they were exhausted. They
were made of an ironwork crown, to which was attached a
bit, edged both sides like a knife and sharp-pointed like a
lancet, so that it would prick and cut the tongue as they were
pulled along. On top of the crown was a bell to jingle, in
imitation of a Mass-bell, when they were forced to their
knees; and inside the crown were spikes to prick out their
eyes and screws to pierce through their brains.

The terror which these details had engendered had been
demonstrated when, during morning service at St Mar-
garet's, Westminster, a mad woman who lived nearby and
was devout in her attendance suddenly, following the stream
of her own thoughts, called out: 'Whores! Whores!' Several
of the congregation mistook it for 'Wars! Wars!' and thought
it a signal that the doom was upon them. Not only did the
service end in confusion amid cries of 'The Papists! The
Papists are come to cut our throats!' but many were prepared to swear that they saw naked swords in the churchyard
and heard the boom of the cannon.

Zuylestein had noticed with some satisfaction that the
attendance at the firework display was scantier than might
have been expected and assumed that the more timid of the
citizens had believed the more recent rumour that its real
purpose was to act as a signal to the soldiers on Hounslow
Heath to fall upon London and put all citizens, men, women
and children alike, to the sword.

A few days later, the Dutchman waited on the King and Queen to take his farewell of them and to receive their letters for William. James wrote curtly: 'I have had yours by M. Zuylestein, who has, as well as your letter, assured me of the part you take on the birth of my son. I would not have him return without writing to you by him, to assure you I shall always be as kind to you as you can with reason expect.' But Mary Beatrice was less formal: 'The compliments M. Zuylestein made me from you, and the letter he brought, are so obliging that I know not which way to begin to give you thanks for it. I hope he will help me to assure you that I am very sensible of it and that I desire nothing more than the continuance of your friendship, which I am sure mine shall always one way deserve—by being, with all sincerity imaginable, truly yours.'

When William opened the letters, he threw them laughingly over to his friend, with 'Well, is the brat the Queen's?'

'Undoubtedly,' said Zuylestein, 'but fortunately not one in a thousand believes it by now.'

'So the Invitation tells me.'

'I know. Have you discontinued official prayers for it?'

'No.'

'Why not?'

'I waited for you to confirm it. I do not trust traitors, even when I have to use them. . . . Can you convince Mary?'

'I was careful to bring her a special message from the Bishop of London,' said Zuylestein, 'whose opinions, I believe, have great weight with Her Highness.'

However, it was some days before Mary was able to confide to her blue and gold diary: 'I bless my God who has decided between the daughter and the wife and showed me, when religion is at stake, that I should know no man after the flesh, but wait the Lord's leisure.'

Sunderland was playing bassett when the King sent for him. It was annoying, because he was having a run of luck; but he decided that, at this moment, it would be unwise to keep James waiting, so he pocketed his winnings and, with his usual leisurely grace, made his way to the Royal apartments. As he went through the Long Gallery he hummed the popular air of the moment, *Couragio*, which, as soon as he was out of earshot, the guard at the further end took up. It was an infectious tune and, the guard decided, would be the rage now that it had the approval of the fashionable Secretary of State.

James's face was bleak as he handed Sunderland a letter, which the Earl saw with dismay was in his wife's handwriting.

'What have you to say to this, my Lord?'

'Has my wife the audacity to presume to use your Majesty as a post-boy?'

'If you read it, you will see that the letter is addressed to Mr Sidney.'

Sunderland's handsome face clouded. There was a hint of reproach in his voice as he murmured: 'Your Majesty is aware——'

'No,' James interrupted. 'I am not aware how the Countess, your wife, came to have knowledge of our plans for the fleet nor why she should trouble to communicate them to Mr Sidney.'

The King's tone denied comfort, but Sunderland in desperation realized that there was no other defence to play. He hardened his own voice: 'You know, sir, enough of my misfortune to know that I am not in my wife's confidence.'

'Nor she in yours?'

'Is your Majesty suggesting that I am capable of doing what even the basest wretch alive would shrink to do?'

The vehemence of his voice and his clear, steady eyes checked James's mood. This man, who had given up everything for the Faith, had knelt with him at Mass this morning.

'No, my Lord. I merely show it to you.'

'The thing is a forgery—but a clever one.'

'It might be, were the information false.'

'How did your Majesty obtain it?'

'One of Chiffinch's men intercepted it.'

'The gossip may have come from the Admiralty.'

'I trust not.'

'We can trace it, your Majesty, in time. Believe me, I will spare no effort; since it seems my own honour is at stake.'

He waited for James's denial which did not come. Remembering that Sidney, years ago, had been dismissed from James's own household for having made love to his first wife, he decided to return to his first line of defence and emphasize it inescapably: 'Though I do not in my heart think that your Majesty can believe that I would make a confidant of a man who has injured my honour in the tenderest point, of the man whom, above all others, I ought to hate!'

'Of course not,' said James, convinced. 'I will leave you to deal with your wife.'

On July 29, the first copies of a new ballad, hot from the secret presses were widely, but discreetly, distributed in London. Though, written to a popular tune, it was easy to memorize, it was as well to have plenty of time for it to be learnt and communicated to the rest of the country.

> Come, come, great Orange, come away
>   On thy august Voyagio;
> The Church and State admit no stay
> And Protestants would once more say
>   Couragio! Couragio! Couragio!
>
> Look sharp, and see the glorious Fleet
>   Appear in their Voyagio;
> With loud Huzza's we will them greet,
> And with both arms and armies meet
>   Couragio! Couragio! Couragio!
>
> Then welcome to our English shore;
>   And now I will engage -io
> We'll thrum the Babylonish Whore
> And kick her trump'ries out of door
>   Couragio! Couragio! Couragio!
>
> When all is done, we then shall hope
>   To see by this Voyagio,
> No more Nuncio, no more Pope,
> Except it be to have a Rope
>   Couragio! Couragio! Couragio!

D

The month ended torrentially with a heavy rain which lasted unbrokenly for twelve hours. To Windsor a courier wet to the skin brought letters forwarded post-haste from London. Both the King and the Queen wrote at once to Mary. James merely enquired what offence had been given that his son was no longer prayed for in her chapel at the Hague. But Mary Beatrice could not contain her sorrowful anger. 'You are not so kind as you used to be,' she wrote, 'and the reason I have to think so is (for since I have begun I must tell you all the truth) that since I was brought to bed you have never once in your letters to me taken the least notice of my son, no more than if he had never been born, except in that which M. Zuylestein brought, which I look upon as a compliment that you could not avoid, though I should not have taken it so if ever you had named him afterwards. You have for him the last indifference.'

The ink was not dry on the letter before another courier arrived, this time from Richmond, with news that the Prince of Wales was dying.

VII

Politics at the Hague

A T the Hague, Dr Gilbert Burnet had never been busier. Quite apart from his private concerns in trying to induce a wealthy widow to become his second wife, keeping a voluminous diary which he intended eventually to turn into a history of his own times, writing the third volume of his *History of the Reformation in England* and keeping himself *au fait* with all the business of the Court, William had now entrusted him with drawing up the official 'Declaration of the Prince of Orange' and writing a pamphlet on the origin of the supposed Prince of Wales, of which he intended to print a first edition of 80,000 for immediate dissemination in England.

But Dr Burnet enjoyed work. He was, in fact, never happy unless he was writing or talking. As the son of a wealthy Edinburgh lawyer and a pious Presbyterian mother, he had, from his earliest years been accustomed to it. Nowadays he never preached for less than an hour and he usually managed his peroration so skilfully that, when he sat down to mop his face, the congregation hummed for him to rise and continue for another half-hour. His bitter anti-Catholicism, involving him at home in two charges of treason, had resulted in an exile during which, to prevent James's attempts to extradite him, he had taken Dutch nationality, after a tour of Europe, which had provided material for a book devoted to contrasting the misery of life and conditions in Catholic countries with their splendour and happiness under Protestant rulers.

At forty-five, Burnet's great bulk and eupeptic countenance expressed with some accuracy that pachydermous insensitivity which, in his earlier years at the court of Charles II had initially given him almost the status and privileges of a jester. His tactlessness was on an epic scale which made it more valuable than tact; for with his boisterous spirits, his boastfulness and his vanity, his audacious stupidity and his spectacular indiscretion, he could achieve results unattainable by the most skilful diplomat.

When, years ago, James had announced his conversion to Catholicism, Burnet had immediately pointed out that his manner of life should have prevented him giving himself religious airs and enquired whether he had seduced the nun who was concerned in his change of faith. James had been startled into a silence which Burnet interpreted as meek acceptance of the reproof. And only recently, at the Hague, when Mary, to whom he acted as spiritual adviser, had brought herself to formulate the question which for so long had troubled her: 'How could my father make my mother a Papist?' he had answered cheerfully: 'He caught Henry Sidney a-bed with her and then had the power to make her do anything.' William, who had been sitting by the fire a little apart from them, had not been able to resist interrupting with: 'Pray, Madam, ask the Doctor a few more questions.'

This morning, however, it was the Doctor who had to ask
her a question. William had interrupted him in the middle of
his pamphlet—in which he had contrived skilfully to weave
four mutually-contradictory theories of the origin of the
supposed Prince of Wales—and sent him to Mary to broach
a matter which, in all the years of their marriage, he himself
had not cared to mention. It was to be mentioned now only
because it had become urgent.

Mary received Burnet with the mixture of affection
and deference she always showed him; for their relationship paralleled almost exactly that between his friend,
Henry Compton, Bishop of London, and her sister
Anne.

'Your Highness will give me leave to speak very frankly?'
he asked.

'Of course. Though if you are come to reprove me for
the time I spent yesterday at play——'

'I have come on a matter of state which concerns the
Prince.'

'Then could not my husband himself spare me the time to
deal with it?'

'It is a matter which concerns him too nearly for him to
care to open it with you.'

Seeing Mary's look of unfeigned astonishment, he added
quickly: 'When—if—you even come to the crown of
England, what do you intend that the Prince shall be?'

'What he shall be?' replied Mary, even more puzzled.
'What should he be?'

'What title?'

'If I am Queen, he will be King. Whatever is mine, is

also his by right of marriage.' Mary could make no sense of the Doctor's questions.

'Unfortunately, that is not so,' said Burnet. 'It is you who, by law, will succeed to your father's crown. You will be Queen Regnant as your namesake the first Mary was Queen Regnant. But her husband, Philip of Spain, was not King. He was King-Consort only, so that, when she died, he ceased to have any standing in the realm.'

'I had not at all realized that.'

'But it is so and you can understand that a titular kingship is not a very agreeable thing for a great Prince.'

Mary remained silent, glimpsing at last implications that had escaped him.

'If you would bring your mind to it,' continued Burnet relentlessly, 'You could be content to remain his wife and promise to give him the real authority as soon as it comes into your hands.'

'I could do that,' said Mary in such a tone that Burnet was not certain whether it was a question or an assent. He went on to explain that, when the time came, she could easily induce Parliament to bestow the kingship on him or even, by her own legislative act, transfer the government to him.

Her slow brain was suddenly racing. What might have seemed the last of William's cruelties was really an act of providential release. If he were to be king in his own right and not through her, then she was relieved of all responsibility of an action against her father and her new-born brother. Burnet mistook the meaning of the slight smile which started to lighten the heavy, prematurely old face. He continued quickly: 'But of course Your Royal Highness ought to consider well before you announce any such resolution; for, once it is announced, it cannot safely or easily be retracted.'

'I want no time for consideration,' said Mary. 'It is enough that I have an opportunity for showing my regard for the Prince, my husband. Tell him what I say; and bring him to me that he may hear it from my own lips.'

When Burnet returned with William, she said: 'I did not know till just now that the laws of England were so contrary to the laws of God.'

William nodded, but said nothing. She was disappointed. She had prepared that opening carefully and, a little proud of it, was hurt that he did not ask her what she meant. She had to add the explanation unasked: 'I did not think that the husband was anywhere enjoined to be obedient to the wife.'

William still said nothing.

'I promise you, William, that you shall always bear rule.'

He bowed, but mechanically, as one acknowledging a deserved and expected tribute.

'In return I ask only this—that, as I shall observe the precept which bids wives obey their husbands, so you will observe that which bids husbands love their wives.'

'Thank you, Mary,' he said and left the room.

With Burnet she discussed the details of her decision and of the possible necessity to consult Anne, but he insisted that these could wait until they came within the region of the practical. He was anxious to talk to her about her pretended brother and to test her reactions to some of the passages he meant to put in his pamphlet.

There was no doubt about his success. Mary wrote in her

diary: 'To think that my father should be capable of so horrible a crime and that, humanly speaking, there is no other way of saving the Church and State than that of my husband going to dethrone him by force, are the most afflicting reflections and would be unbearable without the help of God.'

William was immersed in a more difficult problem. Mary's surrender of her birthright to him had always been only a matter of time and he regarded it merely as a necessary formality. Its implications and the legal business it entailed could be dealt with at leisure. What was immediately urgent was to present a case to the Catholic rulers of Europe so that they might regard him as their own champion against the hegemony of France. In this way, he might completely isolate James and, by a masterstroke, alienate even the Pope himself from the King who had staked everything on the Faith.

The Pope, Innocent XI, an Italian now in his seventy-eighth year, had been engaged, during the whole of his pontificate, in an unrelenting struggle with Louis XIV, in which spiritual and temporal issues had become inextricably intertwined. The devotion of the French clergy to their King was extravagant enough to threaten a schism which would erect in Europe yet another national church independent of the Holy See. Gallicanism would follow in the steps of Anglicanism. Six years previously—in 1682—the French clergy in solemn assembly had issued the 'Declaration of the Clergy of France' which limited the authority of the Pope in favour of that of the King and the national Bishops, who were to be appointed by him. Innocent had immediately condemned their proceedings and refused to recognize the bishops of Louis's choice.

Louis, who was completely devoted to the Faith and, in fact, more orthodox than most of the intriguers who surrounded the Pope, had answered by giving public evidence of his devotion. By revoking the Edict of Nantes which had hitherto protected the Huguenots, he had ceased to tolerate heresy in France. Innocent, far from approving, had openly deplored this move, with its resultant pressure for conversion on the Huguenots, and remarked that 'men must be led to the temple, not dragged to it.'

In 1687, Innocent had further exacerbated Louis by informing him that he could not allow the new French Ambassador to enter Rome unless he surrendered the diplomatic privilege by which the immunity of embassies could be used for political sanctuary. Thereupon the French Ambassador had entered Rome at the head of eight hundred soldiers and had taken forcible possession of the ambassadorial palace. Innocent had said: 'They trust in chariots and in horses; but we will call upon the name of the Lord,' and had not only excommunicated the Ambassador but laid under an interdict the whole of the French quarter and the church in which the Ambassador had officially attended High Mass.

Thus, at every turn, Louis had found himself consistently checked by Innocent, who saw in opposition abroad the only way effectively to weaken the King's authority at home, and their antagonism became so bitter that it was said in Rome that 'if the Apostles were to come again by way of France, they would not be believed here.' And in that very month of

July, 1688, a fresh crisis arose. A new Archbishop of Cologne
was being elected, who, by virtue of his office, would be
both an Elector of the Empire and the temporal ruler of the
important surrounding territory. Neither the candidate
supported by Louis nor his rival, the nominee of Innocent,
obtained the necessary number of votes—though Louis's man
polled more than his opponent—and the decision fell, by
custom, to the Pope, whose verdict was a foregone conclusion. Though Europe was speculating whether French
'cannon-law' would have anything to say on the matter,
Louis was at the moment contenting himself with an official
protest in which he complained of the injustice with which
France was always treated by the Holy See and suggested
that the role of the Papacy was to be an impartial parent to
all parts of Christendom. But it was widely—and, as it
happened, correctly—rumoured that he intended, by way of
reprisals, to seize the Papal territory of Avignon.

In the circumstances William estimated that the Pope's
approval for any move against Louis might be taken for
granted. It might also be assumed that Innocent's opposition
to Louis included an opposition to Louis's only ally, the King
of England. James, indeed, was in an additionally weak
position; for he was now relying mainly on his Jesuit advisers
—his confessor, Father John Warner and Father Edward
Petre, the most trusted member of the Privy Council—
while at the Vatican Jesuits were anathema, partly because,
knowing Louis's essential orthodoxy they tended to be pro-
French and partly because Innocent in his old age relied
chiefly on three heretical Jansenists who were endeavouring
to bring about the destruction of the whole Society of Jesus.

With all these things in mind, William drew up a special declaration to the Catholic sovereigns of Europe. He pointed out the dangers to which they were subjected by French power and ambition and the necessity of rescuing England from vassalage to France. He disclaimed all bigotry and suggested that the real enemy of Catholicism in England was James's foolish policy, menacing both law and property, which, if it was allowed to continue unchecked, might so raise Protestant fury that there would be a popular and uncontrollable outbreak of barbarous persecution of all Catholics. In fact, the averting of such an outbreak was one of the chief objects of William's intended expedition. If he succeeded, he would make it his first care to protect all English Catholics, who would be the real gainers from his triumph. William had little doubt that his argument, quietening uneasy consciences, would be accepted as exactly meeting the international situation.

VIII

A Child's Life

T HE urgent summons which had been received at Windsor was urgently answered. James and Mary Beatrice, who was crying uncontrollably, set out at once for Richmond in their lightest and fastest coach; but the King sent a faster messenger ahead with the request to Lady Powis. Unless the Prince of Wales was still alive, she was to send a courier to meet them before they crossed the river so that they could turn back and be spared, at that moment, the added grief of seeing their child dead.

But there was no one at the river and, though Mary Beatrice gripped James's hand with fear at every horseman they passed, the boy was living when they arrived at Richmond. They stayed with him through the night but in the morning, as he seemed better, they returned for the day to Windsor. There they found packets from Rome—a gracious letter to Mary Beatrice from the Pope, rejoicing in the child's birth and allowing himself to be named as its godfather, and for the King a particle of the relics of the crown of thorns of St Achatius.

Before returning to Richmond, the Queen wrote to Innocent: 'As great as my joy has been for the much-sighed-for birth of a son, it is signally increased by the benign part which Your Holiness has taken in it, shown to me in such tender marks of affection in your much-prized letter, which has rejoiced me more than anything else.' It was the letter of an Italian to an Italian but there was no exaggeration in it. The Papal letter gave promise of a new and happier hope. The child, aided by Innocent's prayers and the relics of the saint, would recover.

But James, though he prized both no less than Mary Beatrice, remained intolerably troubled. He was facing the gravest decision of his life. By comparison, all his previous moments of choice seemed simple. The curt command by which he had won a great sea-fight; the sudden turn and drive at a perceived weakness or the stand against odds which were his soldiership; the long discussion, weighing all counsels and considerations, which preceded a political move; the stubborn act of faith which gave courage to refuse the way of worldly wisdom—these suddenly seemed easy in comparison with what might be demanded now. Nor were there any surrounding circumstances of excitement or grandeur to charge the atmosphere with a sense of occasion and, by that very disturbance, to aid vision. Only the quiet of a child's sickroom.

On the way back to Richmond, he spoke very little and kept tightly in his hand the gold box in which the portion of thorn lay. By the time they had arrived at the nursery, he had made his decision.

The Prince of Wales had not sustained the brief recovery of the morning and life had nearly gone. James ordered that a silk bandage be brought. In it he carefully wrapped a portion of the relic and himself bound it, with a tenderness which surprised the nurse, round his son's blotched forehead. Mary Beatrice prayed audibly. The three doctors, as all eyes in the room were fixed on the royal group, thought it safe to smile quickly at each other and shrug their amusement at the pathetic superstition. He turned to them so quickly that they had only just time to smoothe their faces to deference.

'Gentlemen,' he said, 'it would be useless to invoke the aid of Heaven if we had neglected any human means of aid. I have therefore decided that the Prince is to be fed at the breast. Lady Powis will send to the village for a wet-nurse.'

James had spoken very quietly and the doctors' agitated clamour broke the stillness like a thunder-clap. They refused to be responsible any longer . . . His Majesty, with great respect, had no idea what he was doing . . . The baby would die immediately it tasted milk . . . All the best medical opinion in Europe was against His Majesty . . . Her Majesty would not forget that breast-milk had been diagnosed as the cause of the death of her earlier children. . . .

Mary Beatrice stood close to her husband, her nails digging into his hand. He spoke now rather to reassure her than to quiet the doctors.

'I have not, gentlemen, taken this decision lightly. I acquit you of all consequences from this moment. My son's death will be on my head. But'—he put his arm round his wife, speaking straight to her—'by God's mercy he will live.'

Lady Powis had acted at once. Within an hour, the young wife of a local brickmaker was in the nursery, a healthy red-cheeked girl, in a cloth petticoat, old shoes and no stockings, a little abashed among the grandeur. But her uncertainty

vanished the moment she took the Prince in her arms and
gave him her breast. She was queen there, while the Queen
watched her with envious eyes.

The Princess Anne, who when the Court left London had
gone to Tunbridge Wells, was almost beside herself with
frustrated curiosity. She had heard all the rumours that the
Prince was dying but could come to no firm conclusion
which she could report to the Hague. She realized the
importance of accuracy at this moment, as she particularly
did not want Mary to be angry with her and discontinue the
exciting correspondence. She decided to send her equerry,
Colonel Sands, to Richmond publicly to deliver a compli-
mentary enquiry about her brother's health and privately to
make whatever use he could of his time to discover what was
happening there.

Sands arrived just after James and Mary Beatrice. He
noticed that the Queen's eyes were swollen with weeping
and concluded that the Prince was dead. The fact that he was
not admitted into the nursery raised his suspicions, which
were increased by the sudden departure of a party for the
village and its return with someone in a coach. About the
whole house was an atmosphere of crisis and secrecy. No one
would tell him anything or paid much attention to him.
Standing in a corridor, he noticed the doctors leaving the
nursery deep in angry and animated conversation, but he
was not near enough to hear what they said. The King and
Queen also came out, both looking preoccupied. As soon as
they had disappeared from sight, he stole up to the nursery
door, cautiously pushed it open and, finding no one but

Madame de Labadie one of the day nurses kneeling beside the cradle with her back to him, tiptoed inside.

But before he could reach a vantage point from which he could actually see the baby, the inner door opened and the under-governess Lady Strickland came out. She could hardly believe her eyes and—as he put it when he reported the affair to Anne—'in a great passion asked him angrily "what he was doing in the Prince's nursery" and, without waiting for a reply unceremoniously pushed him out.'

In the corridor he met the King again, now unwontedly cheerful, and took the opportunity to explain his presence by delivering Anne's message. James expressed his gratitude for it, invited him to dinner and promised that afterwards he should see the Prince for himself, so that he could report to her how miraculously her brother had recovered. The new diet they had at last tried had proved successful and there was little doubt that in a few days the Prince would have made a complete recovery.

When at last the Colonel was admitted to the nursery, he saw in the royal cradle a contented baby, playing with the fringe of the cradle quilt. All his doubts were dispelled. This was obviously yet another substitute for the child who had died just before he had arrived and which had been smuggled into the nursery practically under his nose.

The doctors spent the following day securing the services of two other wet-nurses who, when the position was explained to them, were quite happy to concur in the arrangement that they would repay the doctors a substantial percentage of the gifts and remuneration they would receive when they were officially appointed to the Prince. Lady Powis received them graciously and asked for samples of their milk. These she took, with a sample from the brick-maker's wife, to the doctors and, without specifying which was which, asked them to pronounce on the best quality. They unanimously chose that of the brickmaker's wife.

In the country there were now nine versions of the origin of the Prince of Wales. He was the Queen's son by the Papal Nuncio. He was the Queen's son by James's principal equerry. He was the Queen's son by the Lieutenant of the Tower. He was the son of a master-workman in St James's Palace, who had been smuggled in on the day of his pretended birth. He was the son of a priest's whore. He was the son of Father Petre by Mistress Betty at Bath. He was the bastard of a serving-girl in the palace who was thereupon kidnapped and murdered by the Queen's orders. He was the son of the brickmaker at Richmond, smuggled into the palace in a warming-pan, and later returned to his mother for nourishment at Richmond.

And the Richmond story, passed from Sands to Anne and from Anne to Mary and from Mary to Burnet was, in Burnet's skilful hands, capable of several other and subtler versions.

James ordered the remainder of the relics to be exposed in the Chapel Royal for the veneration of the faithful.

IX

The Duke of Berwick

A WEEK after the Prince of Wales's complete recovery, James paid a state visit to Portsmouth of which his eldest son was Governor. Berwick took the opportunity to receive him with special magnificence and turn his inspection of the fleet there into a popular demonstration of loyalty. He was careful in his conversations with his father to make no reference to his private uneasiness about some of the troops.

The King himself, however, in broaching the subject of the Irish regiments who were arriving in England as reinforcements for the army, gave him the chance he needed. When the King told him that the Irish colonel had brought about fifty men more than his proper quota and invited suggestions as to what was best to be done with them, Berwick asked if he might have them in Portsmouth to distribute among his own regiments.

When, in due course, they arrived, the result confirmed Berwick's fears. One of his English colonels, John Beaumont, whose loyalty he had suspected—and who was, in fact, in William's pay—made a protest, backed by five captains, that it was 'not consistent with our honours to have foreigners imposed upon us without it being complained that our companies were weak or being given orders to recruit them.' Berwick, who divined that the real reason was that Beaumont 'was unwilling to have so many spies upon him' insisted that the order was obeyed, whereat the recalcitrant officers asked to resign their commissions. Berwick wrote to Windsor for instructions and James, surprised and furious, sent down a troop of horse to bring the six officers back for a court martial.

Among those on the Council of War, Churchill was prominent. He was now in direct communication with William to whom six weeks earlier he had sent a secret letter by Sidney declaring that he was determined, come what might, to perform his duty to God and his country and that therefore he put his honour absolutely in the hands of the Prince of Orange. He now saw a way to serve his master to whom this incident was potentially dangerous. Beaumont was obviously a fool who was better out of the way and if James could be persuaded to pass the death-sentence on him, it would provoke an additional outburst of hatred against the King in a country which regarded the Irish as objectionable savages. The 'Six Officers' would become venerated as martyrs to such an extent that even the fame of the 'Seven Bishops' would be eclipsed. Though the maximum sentence which a court martial was empowered to pass in such circumstances was cashiering, Churchill urged that, at such a moment, the officers' disobedience merited death. The King appreciated Churchill's enthusiasm, but refused to do more than confirm the correct sentence. The Faction had to be content with a semi-martyrdom, though the pamphleteers did their best with it by inventing stories of torture to which the officers were said to be subjected during their captivity.

Berwick, however, decided that, on balance, the good outweighed the bad. If this affair had never happened, some other circumstance would have served the agitators. It had given him the pointer he needed and, without a court martial, he made some further dismissals, so that he could be sure that, whatever might happen elsewhere, Portsmouth, second in importance only to London, would be garrisoned by loyalists. The pace was quickening. The Dutch Ambassador had just returned to England with formal complaints about Sir Bevil Skelton.

X

Warnings

S IR BEVIL SKELTON, James's Ambassador to Louis, had before his promotion to Versailles been his Ambassador at the Hague, in succession to Henry Sidney. Fanatically loyal to James, Skelton had never been *persona grata* with William, since he was one of the few men in Europe who had no illusions about William's intentions. When he had relinquished his post to the incompetent d'Albeville, he had been careful to leave behind one of his best agents, Bude de Verace, with instructions to watch events in Holland. So well did Verace fulfil the trust reposed in him that he discovered most of the details of William's preparations; he knew the identity of the English traitors, including Sunderland, and he had guessed the probable plan of campaign. This knowledge seemed to him sufficiently dangerous to warrant his leaving Holland at once and he fled to Geneva so precipitately that he left even his cypher key behind. From Geneva he wrote a full account to Skelton, who sent it immediately to James, thankful that here at last was something which the King could not ignore as he continued to ignore the persistent warnings of Louis and Barillon. And so indeed it might have happened, had not Sunderland efficiently intercepted his letter.

The Court of Versailles was in despair at the King of England's blindness. Louis wrote angrily to Barillon: 'I cannot tell by what witchcraft the Court in which you are remains so fast asleep in the danger which threatens it and so ill-informed about what is happening in England and elsewhere.' Barillon replied: 'It is fashionable at Court to laugh at everyone who believes that the Prince of Orange intends to make a descent on England. Nevertheless I have omitted nothing in conversations with His Britannic Majesty and Lord Sunderland to cause them to reflect that the absolutely contrary opinion held by M. d'Avaux cannot be without foundation.'

It was, indeed, a tribute to Sunderland that Barillon should credit him with blindness and James with perspicacity but that neither should suspect the treasonable truth. But, to the King at least, his arguments still sounding convincing. Would William be fool enough to leave Holland undefended with French troops mobilized; and, even if he would, was it possible that the Dutch States General would allow him to? As for discontent in England, there was always some discontent stirred up by the Faction; but was there any man of substance among them who would risk a finger in actual rebellion? One need only remember how bravely they had talked before Monmouth came over and how little they had done once he had landed. As for Louis, he was merely trying to get James on his side against the Pope on the dispute over Cologne. . . .

At Versailles, Louis's surprise at his cousin's folly began to give way to anger; but before he took stronger measures he decided to send a special envoy to make a last effort to get him to see reason. The man he chose was D'Usson de Bonrepaus who had been in England on previous missions and who had at least one advantage over the resident Barillon —that he profoundly distrusted Sunderland. Bonrepaus insisted on seeing James personally and with all the emphasis possible said: 'If your Majesty believes that the Prince of Orange has any other design than to attack you, I am bound to tell you that you are alone in Europe in your opinion.' He then presented him with the draft of a military and naval treaty, with blanks left for the numbers of French ships and troops required to meet the emergency. James refused to sign it and dismissed him with a complaint that he had come to England before receiving an official assurance that he would be welcome.

Exasperated into action, Louis now determined to try to save James in spite of himself. He instructed his ambassador at the Hague, d'Avaux, to inform the States General that he was strictly bound by ties of alliance and friendship to His Britannic Majesty and that any attack on England would be considered as a declaration of war on France, in which event forty thousand French troops would at once invade Holland. The only authorization for this that Louis could claim from the English side was that of Skelton, whose idea in the first place it was and who had actually started to lead a regiment towards the Dutch frontier as the simplest and most practical way of dealing with the situation.

At this point William, seriously alarmed, sent his own

Ambassador (who had returned to the Hague with Zuyle-stein) back to England with indignant complaints.

'Your Majesty' said the Dutchman to James, 'it is very painful for my government to see that you have allowed yourself to be deceived by France and to credit the insinuation that your son, the Prince of Orange, intends to attack you.'

'I have never believed such a thing,' answered the King. 'I trust my son and my daughter completely.'

'But Your Majesty has not only listened to the proposals of M. Bonrepaus, but you have also tolerated the publication of a declaration by M. d'Avaux, so grave, so scandalous and so prejudicial to the glory and honour of Your Majesty that it appears to place Your Majesty under the tutelage of France, making people say that the King of England cannot defend himself against a petty republic.'

'My son, your master, has been misinformed,' answered the King. 'I have honoured all existing treaties. I have not accepted the offers of M. Bonrepaus. The declaration of M. d'Avaux was made without my knowledge or my consent.'

'But Your Majesty's own Ambassador at Versailles, Sir Bevil Skelton——'

'Has been recalled,' said James.

When the Dutch Ambassador left, the King asked Sunder-land: 'What is your opinion of the King of France?'

'Far be it from me, sir,' said Sunderland, 'to presume to say a wa-a-ard against——'

'Of course not, my Lord; but I may say it. It seems to me that my good cousin has excellent qualities; but flattery and vanity have turned his head so that he thinks that no one is safe without his protection.'

'Your Ma-a-ajesty has most pa-a-rfectly expressed it.'

After this final rebuff, Louis kept his troops waiting no longer and ordered them to the war in Germany. Skelton came home, as James had ordered, and was immediately sent to the Tower. It was safe at last for William to throw off the mask.

Exactly a week after the faithful Skelton's imprisonment —on September 24—Clarendon was at the King's levee, where James told him: 'The Dutch are now coming to invade England in earnest.'

Clarendon, adopting the attitude which had become almost *de rigueur* at Court, replied with a smile: 'Your Majesty does not really believe it?'

'I believe it as certainly as I believe you are standing there talking to me now,' said James shortly. 'An express arrived last night with the news that two thousand men have already embarked and seven thousand more are marching to the port.'

'Can it be true?'

'I have no doubt whatever.' Clarendon's impassive face irritated him at that moment and he added unkindly: 'And now we shall see what your Church of England men will do.'

Clarendon, stung, retorted: 'Your Majesty will see that they will behave themselves like honest men, in spite of the fact that they have been rather severely used lately.'

'That is your opinion?' said James and walked away.

Clarendon, as soon as etiquette made it possible, rushed to

Lambeth to give the Archbishop account of the conversation and to discuss plans in the event of invasion. Then he went on to the Cockpit and informed Anne.

He found himself suspecting that she knew more than he did and taxed her with it.

'I know absolutely nothing,' she said, 'except what my husband tells me he hears the King say.'

XI

Letters to Mary

Queen Mary Beatrice to Mary Princess of Orange

Whitehall: 26 September 1688

I am much troubled what to say at a time when nothing is talked of but the Prince of Orange coming over with an army. This has been said for a long time and believed by a great many, but I do protest to you that I never did believe till now, very lately, that I have no possibility left of doubting it.

The second part of the news I will never believe, which is that you are to come over with him, for I know you to be too good. I do not believe you could have such a thought against the worst of fathers, much less to perform it against the best, who has always been so kind to you and, I do believe, has loved you better than any of his children.

King James II to his daughter, Mary

Whitehall: 26 September 1688

I see by yours of the 20th inst. that the Prince of Orange was gone to the Hague; and from thence, that he was arrived. What his business is there at this time, I do really believe you are not acquainted with; nor with the resolution he has taken, which alarms all people here very much.

King James II to his daughter, Mary

Whitehall: 28 September 1688

This evening I had yours of the 24th from Dieren, by which I find that you were then to go to the Hague, being sent for by the Prince. I suppose it is to inform you of his design of coming to England, which he has been so long a-contriving. I hope it will have been as great a surprise to you as it was to me when I first heard it, being sure it is not in your nature to approve so unjust an undertaking.

I have been all this day so busy to endeavour to be in some condition to defend myself from so unjust and unexpected an attempt that I am almost tired, and so shall say no more but that I shall always have as much kindness for you as you will give me leave to have.

King James II to his daughter, Mary

Whitehall: 2 October 1688

I was this morning abroad to take the air and to see some batteries I have made below Woolwich for the defence of the river. And since I came back I have been so very busy to prepare things for the invasion intended that I could not write till now, that 'tis near midnight, so that you might not wonder if my letter is short.

For news, you will have it from others, for really I am very weary; so shall end, which I do, with assuring you of my continuing as kind to you as you can desire.

King James II to his daughter, Mary

Whitehall: 9 October 1688

I had no letter from you by the last post which, you see,

*does not hinder me from writing to you now, not knowing
certainly what may have hindered you from doing it. I easily
believe you may be embarrassed how to write to me now that
the unjust design of the Prince of Orange invading me is so
public. And though I know you are a good wife, and ought to
be so, yet for the same reason I must believe you will be still
as good a daughter to a father that has always loved you so
tenderly and has never done the least thing to make you
doubt it.*

*I shall say no more and believe you very uneasy all this
time for the concern you must have for a husband and a father.
You shall still find me kind to you, if you desire it.*

XII

Conflicting Counsels

JAMES'S first problem was to decide which of his counsellors he could continue to trust. He immediately discounted Sunderland whose advice had proved consistently disastrous, and decided in favour of the Lord Chancellor, Jeffreys, and the Jesuit Privy Councillor, Father Edward Petre, though he realized they were unlikely ever wholeheartedly to agree with each other.

Jeffreys was forty-three, Petre fifty-eight, but the span between them counted for more than a generation. Petre's early formative years had been spent in the early peaceful security of King Charles I's reign when stability seemed permanent; Jeffreys, born into revolution, was four when the King had been executed. Petre, a baronet in his own right and a religious by choice, was devoid of ambition; Jeffreys, of an impoverished Welsh family, was consumed by it. Petre was an amiable man of no outstanding ability; Jeffreys, with a cynical temperament and a caustic wit, had so brilliant a legal brain that he had become Lord Chancellor in his thirties. Petre knew Europe; Jeffreys had never been out of England. During the terror of the Popish Plot, Petre had been in prison, hourly expecting death; Jeffreys had been on the bench as Recorder of London, confidently anticipating promotion.

Jeffreys' immediate reward for his services at that time had had an element of paradox. He had been made Solicitor-General to the unpopular Catholic James. But from that moment he had served him, first as Duke of York and later as King with a fidelity which marked him, at the present crisis, as one of the few Protestants the King could trust with his life. In the country, however, Jeffreys was detested. As one of the Assize Judges on the Western Circuit after Monmouth's rebellion in 1685—later to be called 'Bloody Assizes'*—he had earned the undying hatred of the Faction, and his judicial behaviour had been sufficiently curious to have become a legend. Always suffering from the constant and harrowing pain of stone in the bladder, he was then in such agony that he was quite unfit to take his place on the Bench. The one means of lessening the pain was by drinking copious quantities of weak punch which had had the effect of even further shortening his temper. His quick tongue and loud, emphatic voice were in any case a terror to those appearing before him and, on the Western Circuit where he had been faced with a large number of self-righteous rebels who naturally, in an endeavour to save their lives,

* *The Bloody Assizes* was the name of a deliberately inaccurate work written by a Whig pamphleteer, who was a personal enemy of Jeffreys, in 1689 as part of the victorious Williamite propaganda. The most reliable modern work on the subject, J. G. Muddiman's *The Bloody Assizes* (1929) has shown that the conventional tales of Jeffreys's 'atrocities' have little or no historical foundation and originated in the fertile imagination of Titus Oates. Of the 1,381 followers of Monmouth, lawfully condemned to death for rebellion, about 160 were actually executed.

equivocated and obstructed to the limit, the perpetual pain and the accumulated alcohol had combined to make him a fury of shouting impatience.

If there was thus a comprehensible basis for the unpopularity of Jeffreys, there was nothing against Petre but the fact that he was a Jesuit. Yet to say that was to say all. By popular standards, a Jesuit stood outside the pale of civilized society—a plotter, a perjurer, a potential, if not an actual, murderer. Petre's advice to the King had been, as it happened, usually sound. He had, for instance, urged him not to proceed against the seven bishops and he had implored him not to allow members of religious communities to wear their habits in public as such a proceeding was bound to lead to disturbances among the mob and dislike among the gentry. But whatever Petre said, he was unanimously blamed for every mistake in the Royal policy, as his Protestant detractors found allies in those Catholic circles hostile to the Jesuits, especially the Vatican and the Benedictines.

James was doubly unfortunate in being, at this juncture, forced to rely on two such advisers. In the first place their real unpopularity (which was independent of the excesses of the propaganda that made them the twin bogies of the mob), served to increase his own. In the second, they gave him, inevitably, contradictory advice. The shrewd, opportunist eye of the political Jeffreys saw the worth of making immediate concessions to the Faction; Petre, looking at events from the vantage-point of a timeless Church, insisted that all measures should be submitted to the criterion of a principle. Appease the people, said Jeffreys, by dismissing all

Catholics from their posts. Do this, said Petre, and admit to the world and posterity that your enfranchisement of Catholics was an error. . . .

At the beginning, the King, following Jeffreys, decided to call on the country through Parliament for a verdict on his policy and, during the interim before Parliament assembled, to put everything back to the condition it was in at his accession three years earlier. But on reflection he saw the force of the counter-argument that such a step under pressure would, in men's minds, go far to justify William's propaganda that there were abuses which needed righting; that it could and would be construed as an acknowledgment that he had been wrong to use the Royal Prerogative to secure religious toleration; that it would reveal him as a weak king who could be successfully intimidated and that it would constitute a betrayal of his co-religionists.

It was the last argument which weighed most heavily with James, for here, nakedly, was the temptation he had so long dreaded—to put his Crown above his Faith. He saw the alternative reduced to that simplicity. And Jeffreys, though his phrasing was characteristically his own, recognized it with an equal simplicity when he exploded to Clarendon: 'Some rogues have changed the King's mind; he will yield in nothing; the Virgin Mary must do all.'

One thing, however, the King felt constrained to do to reassure the Church of England that his personal Catholicism did not affect his official support of the legal Establishment. He revoked Compton's punishment and allowed him once more to exercise his office as Bishop of London.

E

With an invasion expected at any moment, the paramount issue, however, was not politics but the Navy. In command of the fleet was the forty-year-old Earl of Dartmouth, 'honest George Legge,' who became a member of James's household sixteen years ago and had served under him at sea. Of his loyalty there was no question; of his competence there was. Admirable in the calms, he had not the vision for a crisis. James, who was in any case chafing that he could not himself lead his fleet, had had too much experience of sea-warfare to try to overrule his Admiral, but he could not refrain from giving him advice.

The entire fleet was ordered to assemble at the Buoy of the Nore and, on October 1, Fighting Instructions empowered Dartmouth to 'endeavour by all hostile means to sink, burn, take and otherwise destroy the armed force of foreigners and strangers' who were bent on invasion. But Dartmouth, waiting for ships at Portsmouth and elsewhere to join him was reluctant to go to sea until he had a numerical superiority. James, who had had a special weather-vane put on the roof of the Banqueting House so that he could see from the window of his room the direction of the wind, urged him to take advantage of the prevailing westerlies. 'Though all should not be quite ready, consider well whether you should lose the opportunity of this westerly wind to get out from among the sands or risk the Dutch coming to find you somewhere near the Buoy of the Oaze Edge amongst the sands; for you must expect they will come out and will be looking for you with the first easterly wind.'

James knew well enough what he would have done. Following the tradition of the Elizabethan sea-dogs, he would have risked everything, letting the wind be a substitute for numbers, sailed to attack the Dutch immobilized in harbour and destroyed the armada by sending his fourteen fireships among them. But the cautious Dartmouth saw only the possible danger of such a course. The wind might change before he reached Holland, in which case he might miss the Dutch on the high seas and so leave the country unguarded. He was still under strength and he needed the rest of the ships and supplies which were on their way so that, whatever happened, he could fight a successful defensive action. . . .

So, unwittingly, he played into the hands of William who, above everything else, was anxious to avoid an action which, whatever the outcome, would be fatal to his cause. The mass of Englishmen, whatever their opinions, would hardly welcome a liberator who came with foreign mercenaries at the head of a foreign fleet which had defeated their own navy. Already some observers were instituting parallels. 'The Dutch in 1688,' it was being said, 'will succeed no better than the Spaniards in 1588.'

All England watched the wind. It remained 'Popish.' But still Dartmouth did not sail.

If James would do nothing about a Parliament and could do nothing about the Navy, there was at least one wrong he could right. He sent for Sir Bevil Skelton from the Tower to apologize for mistrusting him and, in the course of conversation, discovered at last something of the truth about Sunderland. It came as less of a shock than might have been anticipated, for it was merely the confirmation of what he had, for weeks, come to suspect. He found that he was quite calm and able to show no trace of anger when the Secretary came in answer to his summons.

'My Lord,' he said, slowly, 'Sir Bevil Skelton tells me that he sent me some weeks ago very pertinent news from France. The letter never came into my hands.'

'A Secretary's duty, sir, is su-a-a-rely to see that Your Ma-a-ajesty is not ba-a-ardened with trivial correspondence.'

'In my understanding it was hardly trivial. At least you could have given me an account of it.'

'The reason I did not, sir, was that poor Skelton listened to every rumour and reported nothing but second-hand news, on which no reliance could be based.'

'I think not. Events have shown too clearly that he was right.'

'That was past the wit of anyone to foresee.'

'To foresee what Bonrepaus informed me that all Europe knew?' James's voice was suddenly like a whip. 'No, my Lord!'

'I accept Your Majesty's reprimand.'

'I did not send for you to reprimand you but to inform you that you are no longer my Secretary of State and to order you to deliver me the Seals.'

Sunderland, for once, was almost speechless.

'I am dismissed the Court?'

'No, my Lord'—James was calm again—'I do not accuse you of anything more than a lack of judgment so grave as to be unpardonable in a Secretary, so I do not forbid you the Court if you care to come to it. As your last act in office you will prepare the authorization for my friend, Sir

Bevil Skelton, to take up his new post as Lieutenant of the Tower.'

Having done, as he saw it, all that could be done in mundane matters, James gave orders that the Blessed Sacrament should be exposed in the Chapel Royal for the Forty Hours' Devotion so that the faithful, by continuous prayer, might make some reparation for the country's sins.

XIII

Ceremonial Interlude

THE air was too full of portents. Sunday, October 14, was James's fifty-fifth birthday. There was an eclipse of the sun and, when it was over, the wind was seen to have turned 'Protestant.' The cold easterly breeze meant that the new William the Conqueror might land at any moment. No one forgot that the day was also the anniversary of the battle of Hastings. The Drawing Room was crowded as never before and not only out of loyalty.

James himself was unconcerned. After Mass he went into Hyde Park to watch the exercises of the four troops of Guards encamped there. Two young officers, discussing the reliability of their armour determined to test it and fired their muskets point-blank at each other's breasts. Neither breastplate was dented.

Next day, in the Queen's Chapel at St James's, the Prince of Wales (who had been baptized immediately after birth) was solemnly named. The Papal Nuncio, d'Adda, represented Innocent XI as one sponsor; the Queen Dowager, Catherine of Braganza, was the other. Berwick, to whom James had given the Garter a fortnight earlier, was conspicuous among the magnificent throng. The child was named James, after his father; Francis, after Mary Beatrice's brother; and Edward, after St Edward the Confessor, the ancient patron saint of England, whose feast had been celebrated two days earlier.

Outside the mobs sang ditties about the 'P.P.'—the Pretended Prince.

XIV

Anne

IT was only gradually that James came to understand the vital part played in the plot to dethrone him by the story of the bogus Prince of Wales. He had expressed himself emphatically on the subject: 'Those vile forgers of iniquity must certainly think we do not believe in God to imagine we could be such wicked and hellish imposters.' Having said this, he assumed that he had dealt with it. Obviously even their political opponents did not really believe that he and Mary Beatrice were 'wicked and hellish imposters.'

But evidence began to accumulate that the libel was not merely scandalous propaganda for exciting the stupid but the crux of the case. William was coming to England to safe-guard the legitimate succession—that was all. From Holland it was unofficially announced that Mary Beatrice would be allowed to retire to her home in Modena on condition that she restored the child to its mother from whom she had taken it and who, having fled to Holland, was coming over with the Dutch fleet.

Mary Beatrice, when she heard this, thought it amusing enough to go and tell Anne. She was dumbfounded and more than a little alarmed to find that her stepdaughter

answered coldly her laughing question: 'How *do* such
ridiculous ideas that he is not my son get into circulation?'

'It is hardly to be wondered at,' said Anne, 'since those
who should have witnessed the birth were not there.'

From that moment Mary Beatrice, who had passionately
opposed James's suggestion of some kind of official proclamation, on the grounds that it would be derogatory to his
dignity and an aspersion on her character, changed her mind
and withdrew her criticisms; and it was decided that an
attestation of the Prince of Wales' birth should be made by
the witnesses of it before the assembled representatives of
the country.

In the Great Council Chamber at Whitehall, on the
morning of Monday, October 22, the solemn ceremony
took place. The Queen Dowager was there, but not the
Queen, for James had refused to allow Mary Beatrice to
witness so insulting a scene. George of Denmark was there
and may even have believed the lie which Anne had sent to
excuse herself—that she was again pregnant and consequently
would find it too much for her. The Archbishop of Canterbury was there and all the bishops at the moment in London;
the Lords Temporal, the Lord Mayor and the Aldermen, the
Judges and the King's Council, as well as everyone who had
been present at the birth of the Prince of Wales.

'I have called you together upon a very extraordinary
occasion,' said James, 'but extraordinary diseases must have
extraordinary remedies. The malicious endeavours of my
enemies have so poisoned the minds of some of my subjects
that, by reports I have on all hands, I have reason to believe
that very many do not think this son, with whom God has

blessed me, to be mine, but suggest that he is a suppositious child. Fortunately I can say that, by the providence of God, few Princes can have been born in the presence of a greater number of witnesses.

'The reason I have decided to have the matter put beyond doubt in your minds at this moment is that I am expecting the Prince of Orange to invade this country at the first fair easterly wind. You know that I have often risked my life for the nation in the days before I came to the throne. Now that I am king, I consider myself even more obliged to do so and I intend to go in person against him. In doing so, I shall obviously be exposed to accidents. For this reason I thought it best to have this matter settled now in order to satisfy the minds of my subjects and to prevent this kingdom being engaged in blood and confusion after my death.

'I have asked the Queen-Dowager to give herself the trouble of coming here to tell you what she knows about the birth of my son'—here he bowed towards the little figure of Catherine of Braganza, sitting upright and unsmiling in her low chair—'and most of the ladies and lords and other people who were present are also ready to depose on oath their knowledge of the matter.'

Catherine said: 'As soon as the King sent for me to the Queen's labour, I came as soon as I could and never left her till she was delivered of the Prince of Wales.' Forty other people who had been in the bedroom at St James's, led by Jeffreys as Lord Chancellor, then confirmed the event from their own observations—that they 'saw the child immediately after the Queen was delivered and that it was a Prince and had all the marks of being new-born.'

The long testimony ended, James spoke again: 'Now, my lords, though I do not question that all of you here were satisfied in any case of the legitimacy of my son, from what you have heard you will be able to satisfy others. You can see, also, that even if the Queen and I were so wicked as to try to impose a false child on the nation, such a thing would have been, in practice, impossible. I think there is none of you here who will believe that I—who, as is not unknown to you, have suffered something for conscience sake—that I am capable of so great a villainy as to prejudice my own children. I would rather die than do the least wrong to any of my children.'

It should have been unnecessary even in private to state a thing so obvious. He was suddenly surprised at his own voice saying it. The surprise recalled him to the realization that, with these rumours and in this situation, there were no rules; and he added brusquely: 'If any of you think it necessary that the Queen should be sent for, it shall be done.' No one thought so, not even the Bishop of London. There were, it seemed, after all, limits.

But Clarendon, visiting his niece with news of the proceedings, found that with her, apparently, there were not. Anne, who was in the highest spirits because her lie about her pregnancy had been accepted without question, was being dressed by her women. She received him immediately and asked him for an account of the happenings at Whitehall which were, in themselves, a source of considerable merriment to her. Her high, cackling laugh overtopped the constant jokes of the ladies-in-waiting and reduced Clarendon to a state of scandalized incredulity.

'This is no jesting matter,' he said, 'and I shall speak to you of it only in private.'

Anne smiled at Sarah Churchill who, she knew, would mimic this perfectly when he had gone, and answered: 'It's getting late and I mustn't be late for my prayers. I shall be delighted to see you tomorrow.'

When he called again, she indeed saw him for a moment but made so many and so trivial excuses to get away that it dawned on him at last that she had no intention of letting him speak to her. Not till a week later, when news had reached England that the Dutch fleet had been driven back to Holland by fierce storms and Anne was in a panic lest the invasion should not take place after all, did she change her tactics. This time, as soon as he was announced, she came out to him at once with outstretched arms and a welcoming, half-apologetic smile: 'I am so very sorry, uncle, that I have been engaged when you called on me before; but now there is plenty of time. What was it you wanted to say to me?'

'What I want to say now is that I was extremely surprised and troubled the other day to find you talking as you did about the Prince of Wales and, above all, allowing your women to make jokes on the subject.'

'But everybody makes jokes about it. Surely, uncle, you've heard what they're saying?'

'I hear very strange rumours, as every public man is bound to,' retorted Clarendon, 'but there is not the least reason for believing them.'

'I don't say that I believe them either.'

'Then your conduct is all the more strange.'

'The Queen's conduct, while she was carrying the child, was very strange, too.'

'What do you mean?'

'She must have heard all the reports going round that she was not pregnant. You would have thought that, at least, she would have asked me to feel the child in her womb.'

'Did she ever ask you to do so in the case of her other children?'

'No,' said Anne, taken by surprise by this line of attack. 'That's true. She didn't.'

'Then why is it strange that she didn't this time?'

'Well . . . because of the rumours.'

'Possibly she'd never heard the rumours.'

'Even if she hadn't, the King, my father, certainly had. He's been sitting with me here in this very room when he's actually told me the stories that were going round and laughed at them.'

'Well?'

'Well—it seems extraordinary to me that he and the Queen didn't take more care to prove that they were false.'

'Did you tell him that?'

'No.'

'Why not?'

'It was not my business.'

'Didn't it occur to you that if you and he both laughed at the stories he would naturally think that you didn't believe them any more than he did? Even when he gave you the opportunity, you said nothing. If you had the least suspicion in the matter, wasn't it your duty for everyone's sake— quite apart from your own and Mary's—to let him know?'

'He'd have been angry and then God knows what might have happened.'

'If you felt like that there was no need to say it to him yourself. You have plenty of friends who would have done it without bringing you into it at all. *I* would have done it, if you had asked me; but in spite of the opportunities I've given you, this is the first mention you've made to me of it.'

Anne pouted, not prettily.

'Anne,' said her uncle with desperate seriousness, 'do you realize what consequences these slanders may have, even if your father has more sons? It is your most solemn duty to give the country some indication that you, anyhow, don't believe them.'

Anne turned away and said nothing. Clarendon, seeing that he could achieve no more, took his leave, but at the door, he asked:

'By the way, have you had any letters from Mary about this?'

'No,' Anne lied, 'I haven't heard from her for some time and, in any case, we never mention this in our letters.'

Next day, at Clarendon's suggestion, the King sent the whole Privy Council to wait on Anne and present her with a copy of the depositions about the Prince's birth and his own declaration.

'My Lords,' said Anne, with her most innocent smile, 'this was not at all necessary; for I have so much love and trust of the King, my father, that his mere word must of necessity mean more to me than these depositions.'

XV

The Dutch Armada

WILLIAM'S preparations were complete. On the eve of the anniversary of the battle of Hastings, which seemed to him propitious, he took a short official farewell of the States General: 'My Lords, I am going to the navy to embark. I hope you do not take it ill of me that I do not make it known to you all where I am going. I will assure your Lordships that what I am designing is for the good of the Protestant religion in general and of your State in particular, as is not unknown to some of you. I will either succeed in it or spend my blood to the last drop. My Lords, your trust in me and kindness to me at this time is unbounded. If I live and make it not the business of my life to make your Lordships suitable returns for it, may God blast all my designs and let me pass for the most ungrateful wretch that ever lived!'

The Grand Pensionary, replying on their behalf, assured him: 'The States are not at all displeased that you conceal from them your design. They repose an entire confidence in your Highness's conduct, zeal to the Protestant religion and affection to their States; otherwise they would never have given you the absolute disposal of their navy, their armies and their money. My Lord, the States wish you all success in your designs and have ordered throughout all their dominions a public fast and prayers to God for your success.'

The fast was duly observed not only by the Protestants but by the Jews and by the Catholics of the Spanish Embassy, who were—or pretended to be—under the impression that William was attacking France.

Next day, William went to take farewell of Mary, who had been warned in advance by Burnet that 'if there should appear to be any disjointing between her and the Prince, that would ruin all.' William explained to his wife that, if he were killed, it was his wish that she should marry again. Tears came into his eyes. 'It is only the care I have for the Protestant religion that makes me speak like this,' he said.

Mary, quiet and still, said nothing.

'There is no need for me to tell you that it must not be a Papist,' he added. Then his voice broke completely, and he sobbed and clung to her like a child.

Mary was stupefied by this sudden emotion—an unpremeditated act of penitence for the unkind years. She took the little man in her arms and soothed him.

'I have never loved any man but you,' she told him, 'and I shall never be able to love anyone else. Besides, as we have been married so many years now and had no children, I should not wish for a child by anyone—even by an angel.'

William became himself again and was able to talk calmly of the business which must be transacted in his absence and of the people Mary should and should not trust. Then they dined in public with the officers of the expedition—the old veteran mercenary, Marshal Schomberg, who thirty-six years before had fought side by side with James (the same age then that Berwick was now) under the great Turenne; the Count of Nassau, General of the Horse; the luxurious, proud foul-mouthed Herbert who had brought the Invitation from England but whose presence with William was due merely to his hatred of James for promoting Dartmouth instead of himself; the stiff, correct Count van Solmes, William's cousin, who resented the place given to Herbert but saw the necessity for it.

Schomberg was William's deputy who was to take command should anything happen to him and the choice had been made in deference to the States General, which had insisted on some safeguard for their army; but the appointment of Herbert under the title of Lieutenant Admiral General to command the fleet was a political move designed to lessen the danger of a sea-fight. Herbert, as an Englishman, could appeal to Dartmouth's men not to engage fellow-Protestants under an English command and if, by some mischance, an engagement should take place, it could always be represented as a religious contest between two English Admirals.

Burnet, of course, in his new capacity of Chaplain to the expedition was there; and Henry Sidney and Shrewsbury; the Earl of Macclesfield and the Earl of Wiltshire and Archibald Campbell, Earl of Argyle, who having temporarily turned Catholic in an endeavour to persuade James to restore to him the estates confiscated from his treacherous father had, finding the King disinclined for such a bargain, fled to the Hague and bargained with William for a Dukedom.*

* He later organized the massacre of Glencoe.

But the less respectable of the English adventurers were not invited—men like the Cromwellian Wildman, and Harbord, the briber of false witnesses in the old Popish Plot days and the other desperate men who, as d'Albeville was at that moment writing to James, included 'all the rebels and the traitors of the old and new stamp.' The Ambassador added that, in his opinion, 'there is not in Hell a wickeder crew.' The judgment might be too harsh but William, who knew their habit of discussing in detail the forthcoming execution of James and the hanging of the Prince of Wales in his swaddling clothes had no wish for a tipsy incident which might upset Mary. He himself disliked even the more respectable and sat as usual surrounded by Zuylestein, Bentinck and Keppel.

After dinner, Mary drove with him down to the riverside and watched him board the yacht which took him down river to Brill, where he was to embark.

The wind was steadily Protestant when the Dutch fleet set sail on October 19, but next day it turned Popish and settled in the north-west. At night there was a great storm. Through the darkness and all next day the ships struggled in the teeth of it, but at last it was realized that to continue would be destruction. On the afternoon of October 21 the signal was given to return. Some ships were lost and five hundred horses, but the damage was not as great as was reported in England, where for the moment it was believed that the danger of invasion was past.

The same wind took Dartmouth to sea at last. He left the Nore and anchored in the Gunfleet, ignoring James's advice that such a position among the Essex sands, however tactically useful to strike both north and south, was a perilous base at such a time. 'Sir,' he wrote to the King, 'we are now at sea before the Dutch for all their boasting and I must confess I cannot see much sense in their attempt with the hazard of such a fleet and army at the latter end of October. Your statesmen may take a nap and recover, the women sleep in their beds and the cattle I think need not be driven from the shore.'

As soon as the news of the Dutch disaster reached the Admiralty, the Secretary, Samuel Pepys, wrote to him suggesting that he should sail straight to Holland to take advantage of the confusion; but was careful to emphasize that the King left the decision entirely to him 'in regard that you at sea keep better account of the courses of the wind, and more true, than we either do or can do here.'

Dartmouth decided that it was wiser to stay where he was, for the moment, but by October 30, as reports of Dutch re-fittings reached him, and he realized that, sensible or not, they intended to hazard an October crossing, he weighed anchor for the open sea. He was too late. The wind had gone Protestant again and for more than three days he tried in vain to get off the Galloper Sand at the mouth of the Thames. His ships were forced to strike yards and topmasts and two of his frigates, which had managed to gain the sea were driven back, shattered by the gale. While he was thus immobilized, the Dutch set sail for the second time.

William in the frigate *Brill* led the great armada. He flew English colours and, on the masthead, a banner bearing the legend 'The Liberties of England and the Protestant

Religion' under which, in letters three feet high, was the
Orange motto: 'I will maintain.' Behind the *Brill* came the
hundreds of transports and the sixty-one men-of-war
guarding them on each flank, with Herbert bringing up
the rear. As they went through the Straits, the fleet was
seen to extend to within a league of Dover on the one side
and of Calais on the other. At the same moment the men-
of-war at each extremity saluted each fortress—a signal for
all the troops to appear, fully armed, on deck. The martial
music of every trumpet, cymbal and drum, made sufficient
noise to be heard simultaneously in England and France.

To Mary, awaiting news of the expedition, d'Albeville
requested an interview in order that he might deliver a
message from her father. Mary, through her secretary,
refused to see him but asked him to put anything he had
to say in writing. The Ambassador thereupon sent her a copy
of the depositions concerning the birth of the Prince of
Wales. Mary read it and returned it with the comment: 'It
does not surprise me that His Majesty has given himself the
trouble to clear up the doubts on the subject; but I am not
the right judge. I believe Parliament alone can be that.'
Then she went to church and heard three sermons without
any interval.

Every precaution had been taken to pave the literary way
for William's landing. Copies of his Declaration were stacked
in London in tens of thousands to be released the moment he
was known to be on English soil. The Declaration had been
drawn up and written by Burnet and was substantially a

longer and more diplomatic version of the original Invitation. It stressed that William had one and only one objective—the calling of a free Parliament, which should right the mal-administrations of the reign and inquire into the legitimacy of the pretended Prince of Wales. Colonel Lambert, one of the most trusted Orange spies in London, who was in charge of the distribution arrangements, misjudged the time and copies began to appear in London the day before the Dutch fleet actually sailed. Lambert was arrested and thrown into Newgate and a Proclamation issued that all persons were forbidden, on pain of high treason 'to read, write, disperse or conceal any of the said Declarations, but to give notice thereof to the nearest Justice of the Peace.'

XVI

The Bishops once more

THE Declaration, James found, contained only one thing he had not expected. The general grievances of the nation under his tyrannical rule; the appeal to anti-Catholic prejudice; even the reference to his crowning infamy, that 'during the Queen's bigness and in the manner in which the birth was managed, there were many just and visible grounds of suspicion' that not only William, but all good subjects, vehemently suspected that the pretended child was not born of the Queen, so that 'since our dearest consort and our selfs have so great an interest in the matter, and a right to the succession, we cannot excuse ourselves from espousing the interests of the English people and contributing to maintain the Protestant religion, the laws and liberties of the three kingdoms'—all these he noted without surprise. He had become accustomed to them. But the shock he was not prepared for was William's assertion that he was invading England at the invitation of English peers and bishops. This intimation of treachery at home affected him like a physical blow. It surprised him into an instinctive act. He threw into the fire every copy of the Declaration which had been brought to him except one, which he thrust deep in his pocket.

He must have some immediate reassurance, some denial.
The Marquis of Halifax was in town and would do as well
as any for a test. If any had veered to William, it well might
be the celebrated 'trimmer,' whose reputation was to bend to
any breeze. But Halifax, who had no knowledge whatever
of the invitation to William signed by the six temporal peers
and the Bishop of London, was actually reduced to incredulous silence by James's question. Even his wit deserted him
for a moment.

James mistook his silence and remarked on it.

'Your Majesty is asking me,' said Halifax slowly, 'whether
I have committed high treason. If your Majesty suspects me,
then let me be tried by my peers.' Then, seeing in James's
eyes a puzzled protest, he relented and explained, speaking
slowly as to a child: 'If I had committed high treason, how
could your Majesty place any dependence on my answer?
My life would be at stake. Even if I *had* invited the Prince of
Orange over, I should not scruple to plead Not Guilty.'

'My Lord, you entirely mistake me. I do not for a moment
suppose you have committed high treason. The thought
never entered my head. I am merely asking you as one
gentleman asks another who has been slandered whether
there is the least foundation for the slander.'

'In that case, sir,' answered Halifax, 'I have no objection
to aver, as a gentleman speaking to a gentleman on my
honour, which is as sacred as my oath, that I have not
invited the Prince of Orange.'

The King sent next for the Bishop of London. The
summons did not indicate suspicion, though Compton
assumed it did and experienced a moment of panic. Inwardly

he cursed William for having inserted that needless paragraph in his Declaration. However, as William was still in Holland and it was impossible for James to have any proof that the Bishop had indeed signed the Invitation, he decided to treat the occasion as a trial of his steadfastness. It was the Feast of All Saints. As his chaplain had read the opening sentence of the First Lesson at Mattins—'Then shall the righteous man stand in great boldness before the face of such as have afflicted him'—he had instinctively applied it to himself; and in his coach, as it jolted through the mud from Fulham, he had remembered the Dominical injunction: 'Ye shall be brought before governors and kings, but when they deliver you up, take no thought how or what ye shall speak; for it shall be given you in the same hour what ye shall speak.' He trusted that it would.

When James, stressing the words 'Lords Spiritual,' read to him the dangerous paragraph in the Declaration, he found himself able to answer without hesitation:

'I am confident, sir, that the rest of the bishops will as readily deny it as myself.'

'I am sure of that, my Lord,' said the King; 'but since the country may not believe it, I should like a public document from the Bishops as a whole, affirming their innocence and protesting their abhorrence of the action of the Prince of Orange.'

Compton, seeing himself about to be caught in an even more unpleasant dilemma, asked:

'May I see the Declaration, your Majesty?'

But James refused to let out of his hand the one copy he had kept. Compton, secretly amused by the King's ingenuousness, assumed a stiff dignity, as he remarked: 'The document may be a forgery, in which case the matter will require much consideration, your Majesty.'

'Of course,' answered James. 'I shall ask my lord of Canterbury to call you together to arrange everything in due form.'

Compton anticipated no difficulty in dealing with the Archbishop and, as the only other Bishops in London at the time were Peterborough and Rochester (both bitter opponents of the King who, however, had no idea of the issues involved and who thus could face suspicion with a genuine and startled resentment), he agreed with enthusiasm to the royal suggestion.

The Archbishop did not convene them at Lambeth till November 5. The day was appropriate. The mob celebrated it by attacking the Franciscan convent in Lincoln's Inn Fields. Though the friars were rescued by troops, the house was burnt to the ground and its flames topped the innumerable Guy Fawkes bonfires reddening the sky. The King made what reparation he could by touching for King's Evil, with Warner and Petre, both of whom were being burnt in effigy, assisting him with full Catholic ceremonial. The Bishops, piously deplored his tactlessness, gazed across the lurid river and determined their tactics for the morrow.

When, next day, the four of them were conducted into the King's private audience-chamber in Whitehall, the Archbishop began courteously with the prearranged speech: 'Sir, since you have been pleased to say that you are satisfied that we are innocent, we do not regard the censures of others.'

'I am completely satisfied on that score,' said James. 'But where is the document I asked you to draw up and bring me?'

The Bishop of London underlined the Archbishop's argument: 'Sir, we have brought no document, since, with submission, we think it neither necessary nor proper. Since your Majesty is pleased to say you consider us guiltless, we despise what the world may say. Let others distrust us as they may, we rely on our own consciences and your Majesty's favourable opinion.' He made it sound like the peroration of one of his sermons.

James felt sick. This was to be a repetition of the Bishops' tactics in June and now the danger of such cunning opposition was trebled. He counter-attacked at once, in icy tones, with: 'It is not a matter of the peace of your consciences but of the safety of my kingdom. I look upon a public repudiation from you to be an absolute necessity. You, as the Lords Spiritual, are mentioned in the Declaration as having invited the Prince of Orange here. You should satisfy the public, as well as me, that it is a lie.'

'Not one in five hundred believes the Declaration,' said the Archbishop.

'No?' said James vehemently. 'But those ones together are enough to cut my throat—or to bring in the Prince of Orange to cut it.'

'God forbid,' said the Bishops of Peterborough and Rochester.

'Are the Prince's arms on the Declaration?' asked Compton.

James, crushing the paper in his hand, retorted: 'Why

should they be? This is a copy. One of thousands flooding the country. But there is no doubt that it is a true copy.'

'Sir,' said the Archbishop, slowly, 'is it not probable that it is a forgery? The very matter on which we are here proves it false. It says the Prince of Orange was invited by the Lords Spiritual. That, as we know and as your Majesty has agreed, is a lie. Would a great Prince publish a manifest lie and make it the basis of his claim?'

'What!' retorted James, finding it difficult to control his temper. 'Do you seriously suppose that a man who has done what he has done would stick at a lie?'

Seeing the Archbishop at a loss for an answer, Compton hastily interposed to divert the argument: 'The conduct of the Prince of Orange is a matter of state. In your Majesty's treatment of that we cannot meddle. To declare peace or war is not our duty, but in your Majesty's power only. God has entrusted the sword to you.'

James refused to be side-tracked. 'I am not asking you to meddle in affairs of state. I am asking you to declare to the country that you are not in favour of the invasion of the Prince of Orange and his attempt to usurp my throne.'

'Sir,' said the Archbishop, 'we have already made our personal vindication here in your Majesty's presence. Your Majesty has condescended to say that you believe and are fully satisfied with it. Now, sir, it is within your power to publish what we have said in your royal proclamation which, we hear, is about to appear.'

'If I published it,' retorted the King, 'the people would not believe me.'

'The word of a King,' said Compton sententiously, 'is

sacred. It ought to be believed on its own authority. It would be presumption in us to suppose we could strengthen it. The people *must* believe your Majesty in this matter.'

'If they can believe me guilty of foisting on them a fraudulent son, why should they not believe I have invented your protests of innocence?'

'But, sir, all the town will know what has been done and said and we shall own it everywhere.'

'You mean that all the town will know that I have asked you to draw up a disclaimer and that you have refused it.'

'If you will call Parliament,' suggested the Archbishop, 'we could associate ourselves with the Lords Temporal in a denial given publicly in the House of Lords.'

'The summoning of Parliament takes time and now there is no time,' said James. As he spoke, he knew that he was wasting it by arguing further, 'I shall urge you no more, my lords,' he added in a new tone. 'If you will not help me as I ask, I must stand on my own legs and trust to myself and my own arms.'

'As we have at all times adhered to our duty and allegiance, sir,' answered Compton, 'you will understand that we, too, must look to ourselves and we think that our loyalty is less blemished by not being called into question than it would be by any document vindicating it. And as for help, we shall continue always to help your Majesty in the way most proper for us as Bishops—with our prayers.'

James could not trust himself to speak and dismissed them with a gesture.

When they had gone, the King kept the promise he had made some days before to give a sitting to Sir Godfrey

Kneller, who was painting his portrait for Samuel Pepys. To sit there quietly was a relief to him and Kneller, used to his moods, made no attempt to break the silence.

'Tell me, Sir Godfrey,' said the King at last, 'do you think the Prince of Wales is my son?'

'Your Majesty?' queried the painter in surprise, thinking he had not heard aright.

James repeated the question.

'I, of all men, know he is your son and the Queen's, sir.'

'Why "of all men"?'

'You and his mother have sat to me about thirty-six times each, sir, and I know every line and bit of your faces. If it came to it, I could paint you both from memory. And the child is so like you both that there is not a feature of his face but what belongs either to you or to Her Majesty. Even the nails of his fingers are his mother's. I would stake my life on it, sir, even without your word.'

'Thank you, Sir Godfrey,' said James and fell silent again.

Suddenly his secretary entered with an urgent letter which had just arrived. It announced that William had landed at Torbay and, meeting with no resistance, was marching to Exeter.

The King went white and let the paper drop unheeded to the floor. Kneller, fearing he was ill, suggested that the painting should cease for the day. James immediately recovered himself. 'I have promised Mr Pepys my picture,' he said, 'and I will finish the sitting.'

XVII

Lord Cornbury

EDWARD, VISCOUNT CORNBURY, heir and only son of
Lord Clarendon, was a young man of slender abilities,
violent temper and loose principles. As first cousin to
the Princess Anne, he had been brought up to consider that
his fortune lay in her household, in which he was given an
official place. Like Anne herself he soon fell under the
Churchill dominance, and Churchill, shrewdly appraising
him, decided that he would make an admirable tool.
Cornbury, like most youths with eminent and serious
fathers, suffered from a sense of frustration and when it was
proposed to him that the means lay to his hand to eclipse the
paternal reputation and even to outshine his grandfather, the
great Clarendon, he needed little further persuasion. He was
eager to go down to posterity as his country's saviour, the
architect-in-chief of a bloodless revolution.

On November 6 his regiment of dragoons had been
ordered to join Berwick at Portsmouth; and Berwick, on his
part, was then temporarily to relinquish the Governorship
of the town and proceed immediately to take up a command
with the army at Salisbury, pending the arrival of Feversham
and Churchill as Commander-in-Chief and Lieutenant-

General. But Cornbury, though ostensibly he set out for it, did not go to Portsmouth, and Berwick did not receive James's order to go to Salisbury, because Churchill contrived that the Secretary of War should delay sending the King's letter.

A week later Cornbury, with his dragoons, arrived at Salisbury where he found three cavalry regiments with their lieutenant-colonels already in camp. As Colonel, he was thus the senior officer: without question he assumed command and, after resting his own men, gave the order to advance westward. At Dorchester a halt was made and the officers enquired whether they were to find quarters for the night. When Cornbury informed them that, after an hour or two's rest, they were to ride on to Honiton, they were so taken aback that Cornbury's own Major, on behalf of the rest, asked for an explanation and requested to see the official order.

'It is not customary for one in command to show his orders to a subordinate,' said Cornbury.

'Then at least give us some reason, sir, for this long march towards the enemy.'

'We have been instructed to beat up their advanced quarters in these parts. They should not be here in any great strength.'

Though the officers were not altogether satisfied, the march continued. At Axminster Cornbury, who had been expecting a large force which William had promised to send to meet him, dared delay no longer. He ordered sixty of his own dragoons and their officers to fall out in preparation for an attack on Honiton. This was too much for the officers of two of the other regiments who, by now, had realized what he was doing. As they rode up to 'question him roundly,' he spurred his horse and, followed by his sixty dragoons, rode hard to the west. One of the other regiments, whose lieutenant-colonel was privy to the plot, followed; but the other two turned round and, in some disorder, found their way back to Salisbury.

The deserting regiments, arrived at Honiton, found there a large detachment of picked Dutch troops, whom William had sent to receive them; but when the junior officers and men were told they were joining the Prince of Orange, they refused point-blank and would have made a fight for it had they not been immediately disarmed and their horses taken from them by the Dutch. Given the alternative of joining William or making their way back to Salisbury on foot, they unhesitatingly chose the latter; and all that Cornbury could offer Orange was himself and his officers, sixty dragoons, the deserting lieutenant-colonel and the horses and accoutrement of the loyal regiment.

Yet, as a loyalist confessed, 'though the loss was very inconsiderable in itself, yet the consequence was exceeding great, for beside that all the horses of the faithful regiments were so harassed that they were not fit for service for a fortnight, it upset the King's plans, disheartened other troops and created such mistrust that each man suspected his neighbour and in effect rendered the army useless; also, it gave encouragement to country gentlemen who had hitherto been undecided to throw in their lot with the Prince of Orange.'

When the news of Cornbury's exploit arrived at Whitehall, James was in a happy mood. He had just received the Bishop of Exeter, the seventy-three-year-old Thomas Lamplugh, who, in his youth had fought stoutly for King Charles in the Civil War. As soon as news of William's landing had been brought to him, Lamplugh had set off from Exeter to assure James of his loyalty. Now James greeted him affectionately with: 'My Lord, you are indeed a genuine old Cavalier,' and thanked him for making it so plain that at least one Anglican bishop remained loyal. They were discussing the situation in the West when the messenger from Salisbury arrived and Lamplugh, tired from his journey, took the opportunity to retire.

When James had read the dispatch, he asked the man: 'Is that all you have?'

'There is a letter, too, from the Duke of Berwick. He insisted that I gave it to you with a message he said he would not put on paper.'

'What message?'

'He said, your Majesty, that I was to ask you to beware of his uncle.'

'What were his exact words?'

'It was just as I was leaving, your Majesty, that he ran after me and whispered: "Bid my father beware my uncle." That was all, sir. He was in great haste, sir. You will understand, sir——' The man was wretched with embarrassment.

'Yes, yes. I understand. At a time like this, we may all be pardoned for forgetting due ceremony and I am thankful that the Duke thinks like a son.'

James opened Berwick's letter and read: 'I arrived at Salisbury to find that the troops had gone. I followed them and arrived at Warminster (that, I think, is the name of the

F

town) on the evening of this treachery. I was awakened there about midnight by a great noise I heard in the street; and, having looked out of the window, saw a great number of people passing by, who cried out: "The enemy!" Upon this, I mounted my horse quickly and, going out of the town, I rallied the fugitives and brought the four regiments back to Salisbury, of which there were only about fifty dragoons and a dozen officers missing.'

The Bishop of Exeter, as he went along the Gallery to the rooms which had been assigned to him, noticed, without at all understanding the reason, that Churchill and Sunderland were skipping along hand in hand 'in the greatest transports of joy imaginable.'

XVIII

The Eleven Days

I

THE blow had been shrewdly struck. Throughout the past weeks the one thing James had never questioned was the loyalty of the army. It had never occurred to him to doubt that when it came to the push, even if the navy failed to prevent a landing, he would, at the head of his troops, be able to crush William as easily as three years before he had crushed Monmouth. The affair would be another brief rebellion in the west, no more. He had already planned the strategy. With his base on Salisbury Plain, he would advance to a forward line thrown across Somerset and Devon, with Axminster and Chard as the strong points. This *cordon sanitaire* would confine the Dutch disease to the western leg, where it could be dealt with at leisure, while his fleet blockaded the ports of escape. But Cornbury's desertion had revealed an abyss into which everything might fall to ruin. If Clarendon's son could betray him, what certainty was there of anyone? How deep had the corruption gone? Throughout a sleepless night, he tried vainly to shape some alternative plan. Then in the morning—it was Friday, November 16, a cold, grey day with a sky promising snow— he decided to challenge treachery openly. He summoned to

Whitehall all his officers who, waiting to escort him to Salisbury, still remained in town.

He was brief with them. 'Gentlemen,' he said, 'if there are any among you who are not free and willing to serve me, I give you leave now to surrender your commissions and go wherever you please. I look on you as men of too much honour to follow Lord Cornbury's example; yet you may, in conscience, wish to leave me. On my part, I should wish to spare you the discredit of desertion.'

In the momentary silence, each looked at the others. This was the last thing they had expected. Kirke and Grafton turned instinctively to Churchill, with whom, when the King's summons arrived, they had been devising a plan to kidnap him as soon as possible after his arrival at Salisbury and deliver him to William. James was also gazing fixedly at Churchill, trying to read there any sign which should justify Berwick's warning. But on Churchill's face was nothing but a sad frown. For a moment, even tears seemed imminent. Then he fell on one knee and with a gesture whose theatricality was masked by its gracefulness, swore on his heart that he would serve James to the last drop of his blood. The simultaneous 'And I, sir!' of Grafton and Kirke followed so quickly that it sounded like a single echo. The rest protested their loyalty, each with his own emphasis.

James was satisfied. A burden was lifted from his spirit. The contagion of treachery had not spread. The army could still be relied on. It did not occur to him to question the answer or to suppose that soldiers who gave to the word 'honour' more weight than the generality of mankind were capable of meaning other than they said.

'Then, gentlemen, we proceed according to our original plan. At once. The foot will march to Salisbury: you, Colonel Kirk, will take the horse and dragoons as far as Warminster; and establish an advanced post there.'

'You will be with us, sir?' asked Grafton.

'No, Harry. You must be off at once, but I have things still to do here. All being well, I shall follow tomorrow, with my horse guards. At the latest, I will meet you at Salisbury on Monday.'

For a moment, James considered whether he should keep Grafton with him. He had always liked this nephew, who was the most personable of all Charles II's sons. He liked him for his courage, which had given him a legendary status as a duellist. He liked him even more for his honesty, which, on an occasion when James had remonstrated with him about his lack of religion, had made him parry gaily with: 'I admit I have no conscience myself, uncle, but I belong to a party that has a sufficiency.' He had always been open enough in his political antagonism, which made James the more certain of his military loyalty. The only circumstance which the King found curious was Grafton's close friendship with Churchill, for Grafton's mother was the elderly nympho-maniac (now living in Paris with her ninetieth lover) who had kept Churchill in his early days at court.

Grafton and Churchill were standing now, side by side, apart from the rest. On the whole, James decided, it would be wiser to leave them together. Grafton would be party to no move of Churchill's if any were intended. Then he checked even the suspicion of treachery. He was dishonour-ing himself by harbouring it. He returned Churchill's affectionate smile, which dispersed the last echo of Berwick's message: 'Tell my father to beware of my uncle'; and dismissed them all.

By the afternoon, James had completely recovered his equanimity. Two pieces of news, crowding on each other, had cheered him. The fleet, which for the last three days had been becalmed in the Downs, had sailed at last and, with the good north-east wind behind it, was driving down Channel to Portsmouth and the west. And from France came despatches announcing that Louis had formally declared war on William of Orange. So when, after dinner, James saw Clarendon, he was able unreservedly to comfort him. Immediately he had received his brother-in-law's request for an audience, he had realized that he was the man most deeply wounded by Cornbury's desertion and, to shield him from the eyes of the Court, had appointed the interview at Chiffinch's. But he was not prepared for the change in the man. Never an adept at concealing his thoughts, Clarendon's face was a mirror of misery. The atmosphere of assurance and the aura of rectitude which had always faintly irritated James, had vanished, leaving him with the shamefaced air of one who has suddenly in public found himself improperly dressed. James raised him from his knees immediately.

'The fault is not yours, Henry.'

Clarendon grasped James's hand, forgot the speech he had prepared and groaned: 'O God, that I should be the father of a rebel!'

James comforted him as best he could and turned the talk to matters of state.

II

Next day James made his will. It was not a long document. 'Seriously considering the great uncertainty of human life' the King was 'therefore desirous to compose and settle the affairs of our State against the time when it shall please Almighty God to call us from this transitory life.' He left everything to his 'entirely beloved wife and royal consort' and to his 'most dear son, Prince James' to whom 'by inherent birthright and lawful succession' would descend 'the imperial crown of the realms of England, Scotland and Ireland.' Until the Prince was fourteen, he was to be in the 'sole governance tuition and guardianship' of his mother, but the Chancellor and the other officers of state were requested to continue in office in the event of the King's death.

The six Privy Councillors whom he had appointed to advise the Queen and undertake the government during his absence in the field witnessed it—Jeffreys, as Chancellor; the two aged Catholic peers who had once fought for his father in the Civil War, Arundell of Wardour, now eighty-two, and Belasyse, in his middle seventies; the two forty-year-old Scots, Preston and Melfort, who had unavailingly urged him, for safety's sake, to arrest on suspicion all the leaders of the Faction; and the hardworking, necessary Godolphin 'never in the way and never out of the way.'

Together they took the will to the Queen and James formally authorized her and them to act as the regency in case of his death.

When the others had retired and James and his wife were left alone, Mary Beatrice said slowly, not looking at him lest she could not hold back her tears: 'You know what you are asking of me?'

'Yes,' he replied, 'to be what you are—the Queen.'

He did not suppose the words could comfort her, but he could think of nothing else to say. He had to leave her alone in a London on the edge of insurrection, taking her child from her to send him to Portsmouth, for from there, if necessary, the Prince could be taken to the safety of France. And he himself was going to the hazards of a battle.

'If I could only come with you, James!' she said. 'As long as I'm with you, I've no fear. You know that?'

'I shall not be long. We shall have twenty-seven thousand loyal troops at Salisbury. It will be a matter of half a day's battle—if William even gives battle.'

'And you can trust them?'

'They're no Cornburys. It was as well he went. I've given the others a chance to go, too; but it was an insult to do it.'

She was more afraid for him than ever. If only she could have given him a pinch of her Italian mind to leaven that honest English stupidity! She felt, at that moment, older than his mother.

'James, will you promise me something?'

'Sweetheart, yes; for you would never ask anything I could not promise.'

'Promise me you will walk as a man would among quicksands. Where you trust most, suspect most.'

'I will be as careful as I can.'

He could not say more, for the situation was indefinable. She decided not to tell him, as she had originally intended to, that she had found that morning inside her glove a copy of a pamphlet about the Prince and the warming-pan. The circumstance would only increase his alarm for her without making him more careful for himself.

Their conversation was interrupted by a message that a deputation of bishops, headed by Sancroft, had arrived at the Palace to crave a last audience before the King left.

'With them at least,' James said to Mary Beatrice, 'I need no warning.'

This time and in these circumstances, he was unable, even had he been willing, to mask his anger. When Sancroft explained that he had come, bearing a petition signed by some of the Lords Temporal as well as the Lords Spiritual asking for the calling of a Parliament and the making of overtures to William, James turned on him with: 'What time or possibility is there for calling Parliament when there is a foreign enemy on English soil? It is no fit time to call Parliament when armies are in the field. Nor is it proper for me to treat with the Prince of Orange, who has without any provocation, invaded me, against all the laws of God and man.'

'But a free Parliament,' began Compton, 'would——'

'How can any parliament be free,' the King interrupted, 'when an enemy in arms can return a hundred votes?'

Even Compton was surprised at James's intensity. The King continued ruthlessly: 'I could not prevail on you the other day to declare against this invasion; but you are ready enough to declare against me. Then you would not meddle with politics. You have no scruple about meddling now. You first excited this rebellious temper among your flocks and now you openly foment it. You would be better employed in teaching them to obey than in trying to teach me how to govern.'

'But, your Majesty, on the other matter,' said Sancroft, 'bloodshed might be avoided, if you would consent to treat with the Prince of Orange.'

'Not only shall I make no overtures to an invader, but I shall receive none,' answered James; but now his voice was quiet, on a level with the Archbishop's. 'If the Dutch send flags of truce, the first messenger will be dismissed without an answer and the second messenger will be hanged.'

'With respect——'

'And I have no time left to bandy words further with you. These last months you have all said enough and I have listened too much. You are dismissed.'

At two o'clock, the King set out at the head of the household troops and Londoners forgot their religious preoccupations for a moment to unite in admiring the magnificent cavalcade thundering along Piccadilly.

III

Next day, Sunday, November 18, it was snowing hard. James, who with the Prince of Wales had spent the night at Windsor, rose early and, immediately he had heard Mass, gave orders to continue the journey. The Prince, with his nurses and in charge of Lord and Lady Powis, would travel with him as far as Basingstoke, where they would turn south on the Portsmouth road. Portsmouth was for the moment without a Governor, since Berwick was with the army; but as the fleet lay there under Dartmouth, whom James could

trust to the uttermost, it was still the safest place in the
Kingdom. At Basingstoke, when the King had watched his
son take the road to safety, he did not remain long, wishing
to gain Andover, where he was to spend the night, before
the light of the short, bitter day was altogether gone.

In London, that afternoon, Anne sat at her escritoire, with
Compton leaning over one shoulder and Sarah Churchill
over the other, composing the letter which, before leaving,
Churchill had insisted to them she should write to the Prince
of Orange. After many scratchings out and rephrasings, she
made a fair copy: 'Having on all occasions given you and my
sister all imaginable assurances of the great friendship and
kindness I have for you both, I hope it is not necessary for
me to repeat anything of that kind and I shall not trouble
you with many compliments, only in short assure you that
you have my wishes for your good success. I hope my
husband, the Prince of Denmark, will soon be with you to
let you see his readiness to join with you; he will, I am sure,
do you all the service that lies in his power. He went yesterday with the King towards Salisbury, intending to go from
there to you, as soon as his friends thought it proper.

'I am not yet certain if I shall continue here or remove into
the City. That will depend on the advice my friends give me,
but wherever I am I shall be ready to show you how much
I am your humble servant.'

When the three had read it over with approval, Anne
asked Compton: 'Why can't I tell him we are going to
Nottingham?'

'Because,' said the Bishop, making an effort to keep his

patience at having to answer this question for the third time, 'we are not certain that we are.'

'But you said my Lord Devonshire is making Nottingham his headquarters.'

'The Bishop has told us already,' interrupted Sarah tartly, 'that we can't tell when Devonshire will move. At the moment, he is still at Hardwicke. That is so, is it not, my Lord?'

'According to my last report,' said the Bishop, looking at her gratefully. Sarah Churchill might, he reflected, have many drawbacks, but at least she could control Anne, even in her more obstinate and stupid moods. 'And you see,' he added, 'if your letter should fall into the hands of the enemy, they might get suspicious and even prevent the rising in the North.'

He noticed approvingly that there was not the least reaction on Anne's face when he described her father as 'the enemy.'

'But when do we go?' insisted Anne.

'When we get word from Lord Churchill,' said the Bishop.

'Probably on Wednesday,' said Sarah.

'I hope it will be soon,' said Anne. 'Waiting is very trying.'

In the Cathedral at Exeter, that Sunday morning, Dr Burnet preached to William who sat, unable altogether to mask his boredom, on the Bishop's Throne. The congregation, the Doctor noted with pleasure, was larger and more influential than that of the previous Sunday. During the past week, more than sixty men of rank and fortune in the west had come into the city and declared themselves for the Prince of Orange. The atmosphere of the Cathedral Close was now that of a little Court. The common people, too, had grown used to the invaders, even to the two hundred negro slaves whom the English detachment of gentlemen from the Hague had brought over to wait on them and the regiment of Swedes in the skins of bears which they were reputed themselves to have slain. The auditory at Morning Prayer was thus not only distinguished but, in portions, vivid. It was true that no Canons attended the service, but there were several prebendaries and choristers. The only blot on the proceedings was that the prebendary taking the service forgot Burnet's peremptory instructions and, by force of habit, read the prayer for the Prince of Wales. As it was too late to stop him, Burnet waited till the end with lips pursed in readiness and, in place of the 'Amen' made a rude noise which echoed round the silent Cathedral and mightily amused the congregation.

When the service was over, Burnet lifted his hand to stay the withdrawal of the worshippers and William stood up under the episcopal canopy to address them. In his harsh voice, with its Dutch accent, he gave a shortened form of the address which he had made to the gentry of the neighbourhood three days earlier: 'Our duty to God,' he said, 'obliges us to protect the Protestant religion; and our love to mankind, your liberties and property. Though we have a good fleet and a good army to render these kingdoms happy, by rescuing all Protestants from popery, slavery and arbitrary power and by promoting peace and trade, which is the soul of government and the very life-blood of a nation, yet we rely more on the goodness of God and the justice of our cause than on any human force or power whatever. Yet, since God is pleased we shall make use of human means and not expect miracles, we shall with prudence and courage put in execution our so-honourable purposes. Therefore, friends and fellow-Protestants, it is our principle and resolution rather to die in a good cause than to live in a bad one, well knowing that virtue and true honour is its own reward and the happiness of mankind our great and only design.'

The emotion engendered in the congregation was such that Burnet felt that the occasion could only be met by ordering the *Te Deum*, even though it had been already sung at its proper place in the service, to be sung again.

IV

When on Monday James arrived at Salisbury, where apartments had been prepared for him in the Bishop's Palace, he found Berwick waiting there insistent on a private audience before the general meeting of the Council of Officers.

'Of course, James,' he said to his son, 'we shall be private in the bedchamber.'

'I mistrust even the walls in a strange house, father. Let us walk on the lawn, in sight of everyone, but out of sound.'

'That will seem strange enough, this weather.'

'It's not cold now the wind's westerly.'

'What did you say?'

'The wind's changed. The nor'-easter's gone. It's soft weather—though I shouldn't be surprised if we'd a gale by night.'

'From the west?'

'Yes, from the west, of course.'

'Pray God, not that too,' James murmured, so low that his son could hardly catch it. Berwick, who had not realized, as his father had, that a westerly gale now would prevent the fleet blockading William and blow it back impotent to Portsmouth, continued earnestly: 'The weather's in God's hands, indeed, but my uncle Churchill is still in yours. You got my message?'

'Yes; but I could not understand it.'

Pacing together on the great lawn, well out of earshot of the watching courtiers, Berwick poured out his suspicions. Cornbury's desertion was the first move of a concerted campaign against the King. Churchill, Grafton and Kirk, with others possibly, even including George of Denmark, had planned to lead the whole army over to William. It was only the loyalty of the common soldiers which had prevented its happening already.

'Have you any proof of this?'

'What kind of proof?'

'Letters . . . witnesses . . .'

'How could I have?' said Berwick impatiently, 'have you ever heard of a traitor leaving an advertisement of his treachery? But there are too many rumours for it not to be so. And Lord Feversham is certain of it, too. Every order he gives, my uncle Churchill tries to countermand. Father, I beg you to arrest them on suspicion.'

'And justify the lawlessness and tyranny my enemies accuse me of?'

'This is war.'

'Therefore I must trust my army,' said the King, 'but I——'

He broke off as he noticed that Churchill and Grafton had come out of the house and were starting to walk towards them. His arm on Berwick's shoulder, he said quickly and in a very low voice, 'But give me proof of some kind and I will act within five minutes. And I thank you, James.'

They greeted Churchill and Grafton courteously and went back into the house for the Council of War.

It continued—so it seemed to James—interminably. The original plan had become impossible. The invading army already had its outposts in Axminster, so that the west country, where the great ditches were as good as trenches and the thick hedges gave ample cover, was lost. Moreover, the King's artillery had not yet arrived, nor had the Scotch and Irish dragoons, so that the army could not move forward. What tactics would serve? Would it be wisest to fall back on London?

'Is Kirk at Warminster, as I ordered?' asked James suddenly.

'He is there in force, sir,' said Churchill, 'with four battalions—two of Dumbarton's, his own "Lambs" and the Queen's. There is the third troop of guards, two regiments of horse and the Queen's dragoons. May I suggest that your Majesty rides over there in the morning to inspect them?'

'I will think of it.'

'I ask permission to accompany you,' said Berwick.

'We shall all, with permission, accompany His Majesty, my dear nephew,' retorted Churchill.

James found difficulty in hearing this. It seemed to him

that the voices had grown very faint. The heat of the room became suddenly intense. His head was throbbing as if it would burst and a stabbing pain in it made him wince. He put his hand up to unloose his neckband and saw it suddenly redden as a stream of blood came pouring from his nose.

The hæmorrhage—the first he had ever experienced—alarmed his hastily-summoned doctors by its severity. Every known remedy was tried in vain until, in desperation, Dr Radcliffe decided to bleed him from the arm and so by degrees checked the bleeding from the nose.

The attack undoubtedly saved his life. The stress and strain of the last few days, with physical exhaustion combining with mental anguish, had been too much even for his iron constitution; and an apoplectic seizure would have drowned his brain in blood had not his nose acted as a safety-valve. Sitting in the great high-backed chair in his bedroom, weak but calm and in command of himself, he asked George of Denmark to take his place at the head of the supper-table so that the court might not miss the meal; and, for once, George refrained from saying 'Est-il-possible?' but quietly obeyed the command.

But Berwick refused to leave the King and told the Gentlemen of the Bedchamber that he would replace whoever was on duty. So father and son supped a bowl of broth together, while Churchill sent a secret messenger post-haste to London to warn them there that there might have to be a change of plan.

V

Next morning, James had recovered. He felt, indeed, better than he had done for several days, and, without a second thought, refused his doctor's advice to stay quietly by the fire in his own room, leaving Feversham and his officers to make decisions about the camp on Salisbury Plain.

'No, I shall ride there with them and choose the site for the camp myself.'

'Could you not wait till tomorrow, sir, so that we may know that the bleeding has stopped?' Radcliffe ventured.

'We can see it has stopped, Doctor, thanks to your wisdom.' Then, seeing the look of disappointment on Radcliffe's face, he added: 'If you had a patient whose crisis between life and death was expected, would you leave him to a nurse?'

'No, sir. I hope I have given you no reason to suppose such a thing of me.'

'No, you have not. But that is what you are asking of me. I have to place my troops on the Plain so that, if needs be, they can fight there with me to the death. Lord Feversham and General Churchill and my son Berwick are good soldiers, with eyes for position as sure as mine. But I should be failing in my duty if I did not take the final decision myself.'

Feversham, Churchill and Berwick bowed at the compliment, and Feversham said: 'I could take no decision, sir, without you.'

Churchill added: 'And since, sir—if the doctor will allow

me to say it—you look so prodigiously recovered, may I ask that you will ride on immediately to Warminster to inspect the outposts? To save you fatigue, I will have my coach waiting.'

'It would be wiser,' said Berwick, 'if His Majesty decided that when we return from the Plain.'

His tone was so remote and cold that, for the first time, Churchill wondered how much he knew.

The decision, however, was taken out of everyone's hands. No sooner had the party reached the heights of the Plain and were discussing which of the escarpments might be of value and where it was best to place the artillery than the King's hæmorrhage started again with even greater violence and persistence than on the night before. There was no question of any journey except a return to his bedroom.

This time the doctors bled him four times before it stopped; and when at last he dozed off to sleep, he was like a tired child.

VI

On Wednesday, November 21, William received the news that the attempt of Churchill, Grafton and Kirke to kidnap James had failed. Circumstances had prevented the King from entering the coach in which he was to be brought a prisoner to William's outposts at Axminster. Whether or not James would have reached them alive was problematical, since, if any attempt at a rescue had been made, he would have been immediately shot or stabbed. In any case, there would have been no need for William to give battle. But now that the scheme had come to nothing and, according to

Churchill's message, the King was confined to his room by a hæmorrhage, William decided that no more time must be lost and gave the order for the immediate advance of his army from Exeter towards Salisbury.

The great force set out in three divisions to join the advance guard at Axminster, and the countrymen of Devonshire and Somerset gazed at a microcosm of the mercenaries of Europe—Swedes and Swiss and Dutch and Germans—tramping through English lanes. Since their own local gentry and landlords were riding with them, they had no misgivings. If anything, they were grateful that so many soldiers had arrived to protect them against papist cut-throats; and they joined in the marching-song:

> Poor Berwick, how will thy dear joys
>   Oppose this brave voyagio?
> Thy tallest Sparks will be mere toys
> To Brandenburg and Swedish boys!
>   Couragio! Couragio! Couragio!
>
> Stirum advance the Buda blades
>   Thou'st brought in this voyagio:
> And, since the laurel never fades,
> Send our foes to Stygian shades
>   Couragio! Couragio! Couragio!
>
> Thus they the victory will gain
>   After this brave voyagio;
> And all our liberties maintain
> And settle Church and State again.
>   Couragio! Couragio! Couragio!

But even more popular was a newer song, set to the tune of Lilli Bolero, which had a more topical and local allusiveness:

Now to maintain the Protestant cause,
 All the whole West does loyally stand,
For our lives, religion and laws,
 Roman shall never reign in this land.
Stout lads brisk and airy for William and Mary
They'll valiantly fight their rights to maintain.

The first fight took place that day at Wincanton. A party of William's men were sent out to steal horses for the baggage-trains. Under their lieutenant, Campbell, they were surprised by some of James's Irish soldiers under Patrick Sarsfield. They had just time to hide behind the hedges bordering the road before the loyal troops cantered down it. For some minutes Campbell held his fire, because they had by now become accustomed to renegades that they had no desire to hurt potential friends. Eventually Campbell came out of hiding and challenged them:

'Stand! Stand! for whom are ye?'

'I am for King James. Who are you for?' said Sarsfield.

'For the Prince of Orange!' said Campbell.

'God damn me, I'll "Prince" thee,' returned Sarsfield and shot him dead.

There was a volley from the hedges but Sarsfield led his men through them and surrounded the Williamites in the field beyond. They would have taken all prisoner had not at that moment a miller of Wincanton ridden up with the false report that the Prince with his whole army was in sight, which made Sarsfield think it incumbent on him to retire, taking with him six prisoners and leaving nine dead in the field. He himself had lost only two men, but the encounter was immediately reported in the countryside as a victory for a handful of gallant Protestants surprised by an overwhelming number of Papists.

When, at night, the matter was reported to James at Salisbury his lassitude was so intense that Berwick could not be certain whether or not he understood that civil war was again a reality.

VII

The news of the King's sudden seizure was the common talk of the London coffee-houses on Thursday, November 22, and when Clarendon went for an audience at Whitehall he immediately commiserated with Mary Beatrice on it. She was distracted and made no attempt to hide it.

'He has never had such a thing before; at least not since I have known him. You, my lord, have known him longer than I. Has it happened to him before?'

'No, madam, not to my knowledge. But there is no need to distress yourself like this. Many things may cause a bleeding at the nose.'

'But it is not only that. I have talked to Sir William here. It is like an apoplexy. And James is the same age as——'

He knew, without waiting for her to finish the sentence, what she meant. Charles II had died of an apoplectic stroke when he was but four months younger than James was now. He interrupted her:

'We have no reason to suppose, Madam, that his constitution is like his brother's. And the bleeding may have
relieved him. We all know how much strain he has suffered
these last few days. I sought this audience that you might
know how I deplore my son's part in it. The King was
gracious enough to forgive me; and I hope your Majesty
will be, also.'

'You cannot be blamed, my Lord, for what your son did.'

Clarendon thanked her and was about to go when she
stopped him with: 'How can it happen, my lord, that the
King is so misunderstood by his people?'

'In what particular, Madam?'

'They pretend he is against their—your religion; and
nothing is further from his mind. *You* must know this.'

Clarendon nodded the assent he did not wish to give in
words.

'All James wants is that all men should have their consciences free to worship God as they believe right. I cannot
understand how anyone can deny the goodness of that.'

'In England, Madam, there can be no liberty of conscience
unless Parliament allows it. That is our law.'

'But it is so *stupid!*' said Mary Beatrice.

'Nevertheless,' said Clarendon stiffly, 'that is our English
way.' As he did not wish to leave her in anger, he added in
a kindlier tone: 'Your Majesty, I am sure, is the best ambassador between the King and his people and could use your
good offices by bringing about a happier understanding.'

'I have no other wish,' said the Queen, 'but, you see, they
will not let me.' She handed him a pamphlet, containing the
news that 'peace would have been concluded between the

King and the Prince of Orange, but the Queen, with Father Petre and the rest, prevented it. The Queen, like a true virago, beat the King again just before he went out against the Prince.'

'But Madam,' said Clarendon, genuinely distressed, 'you do not take notice of this filth from the streets.'

'I find it difficult not to,' said the Queen.

A news writer, on that Thursday, reported to his correspondent in the country: 'Though there was never more occasion of inquiry for busy, impertinent people that gad about all day long for coffee and news, yet there was never less certainty of what is happening, there being about this City so many engines that are made use of to spread what best suits the purpose of a party. Yet the City of London was never quieter, every man minding his business and securing his debts. The soberer and the richer sort have expressed their dislike of these proceedings which are likely to perpetuate and entail war upon the nation by the removal of the Prince of Wales who is now at Portsmouth and, as some will have it, will pass into France.'

That day had been chosen by Danby and Devonshire to strike in the North. Devonshire, at the head of a powerful armed troop, surprised Derby, accepted the immediate capitulation of the defenceless municipal authorities and proceeded to Nottingham, which he made his headquarters and where by previous arrangement, he was joined by the Earls of Manchester, Stamford, Rutland and Chesterfield with their dependents and retainers.

At York, where there was a small but loyal garrison, more careful measures had had to be taken. Danby, as High Sherriff of Yorkshire, had some time previously appointed November 22 as the day when all the gentry and freeholders of the county, as well as the Deputy Lieutenants of the three Ridings, were to meet to frame an address to the King on the state of affairs in the country. Four troops of local militia, whose leaders were in the plot, had been called out under pretence of keeping order. The Common Hall was crowded with freeholders and the discussion had just commenced when Danby's hirelings in the streets started the rumour that the Papists were in arms and were killing all the Protestants. As the Catholics in York were in proportion of about one to five hundred of the citizens, such a proceeding was not only intrinsically improbable but, in fact, they were themselves, fearing murder, mostly in hiding. But no story of Popish atrocity could be so wild and extraordinary as not to find instant belief and the meeting broke up in panic.

At this moment, with a timing which was the result of perfect organization, Danby rode into York at the head of a hundred horsemen who were immediately joined by the militia, raising the shout: 'No Popery! A free Parliament! The Protestant religion!' The garrison, hopelessly outnumbered and taken completely by surprise, were quickly disarmed; the governor arrested; the gates closed; and the mob incited to desecrate and destroy the one Catholic church in York. Then Danby at the Guildhall read a Declaration which, at the same moment, Devonshire was reading at Nottingham: 'We, the Nobles, Gentry and Commoners of the Northern counties assembled together for the defence of our laws, liberties and properties, being by innumerable grievances made sensible that the very fundamentals of our liberty, religion and properties are about to be rooted out by our Jesuitical Privy Council, do unanimously declare that, not being willing to deliver over our posterity to Popery and slavery, we, by joining with the Prince of Orange (whom God Almighty hath sent to rescue us from the oppressions aforesaid) will use our utmost endeavours for the recovery of our almost ruined laws, liberties and religion. We doubt not of all honest Englishmen's assistance; and humbly hope for and implore the Great God's protection, that turneth the hearts of His people as pleaseth Him best; it having been observed that people can never be of one mind without His inspiration, which hath in all ages confirmed that observation—*Vox populi, vox Dei.*'

At Salisbury James insisted, in spite of his weakness, on calling a Council of Officers. Feversham and Berwick urged that, with the whole of the West now behind William—for during the day they had received the news that the Earl of Bath, in charge of Plymouth, had joined Orange—it was essential to fall back on London. If William, instead of risking a frontal attack on James, made forced marches to cut him off from his capital, the position would be grave indeed. It was an axiom that, in all civil strife, whoever held London won the war. The late Civil War had amply demonstrated that, for it was agreed that the initial error of Charles I had been to leave London.

Grafton and Churchill, on the other hand, were even more insistent that the army should move forward, not back. The only tactics of quick victory were to attack William at once before he consolidated his position. Once James in person appeared in the West, the traditional loyalty of the people would reassert itself and the English renegades who had joined William would immediately come back to their true allegiance. To return to London was folly of the worst kind. For one thing it would spread despondency among the troops gathered on Salisbury Plain, who were now straining at the leash. For another, it would provoke alarm in the capital and destroy among the citizens all trust in James's ability to fight.

Churchill's argument was cogent enough. From the military point of view it was irrefutable and both Berwick and James realized it.

'What have you to say to that?' the King asked his son.

But Berwick wanted time to think. Nothing could move him from the certainty that, as far as his uncle was concerned, tactics had nothing to do with it. He said: 'I should prefer to hear the Commander-in-Chief's answer.'

Feversham, no less distrustful of Churchill than Berwick, remained on the military plane: 'As I see it, sir, the chief matter is London. Everything is subservient to that. Once we safeguard the capital, we can follow Churchill's advice and advance to the West. But we dare not do so, with the enemy so near, leaving London exposed.'

'But,' said Churchill, 'by the time we have retreated and re-formed, William will be at least here at Salisbury, barring our way to the West and cutting off Portsmouth.'

Berwick had now made up his mind and determined to test Churchill.

'I suggest,' he said slowly, 'that we fall back but not as far as London. Only as far as the Thames, which we can use as our moat.'

'Our moat!' said Grafton. 'A barrier to our easy advance.'

But Churchill was more vehement and, because of it, banished all Berwick's doubts. 'It is insanity to retreat even a foot when our way to quick victory lies in advance. Sir, you have been good enough to praise my soldiering.'

James nodded his assent.

'Then,' continued Churchill, 'I will stake all the reputation I have or may ever get that now there is only one road to take—the road to Axminster.'

'I am sure you think so, John,' said the King, 'and it will be no reflection on you if I do not follow your advice.'

'We retreat, sir?' said Feversham.

The silence was tense.

At last James said wearily, as one tired of a game that has gone on too long: 'Yes, we retreat.'

VIII

The decision having been taken, next day saw the breaking-up of the camp. James ordered the army to retire to London by several different routes, for the convenience of quartering and commissariat. Feversham himself, with the main body of horse and dragoons was to base himself, as long as practicable, on Reading, where he was to be joined eventually by Kirke, who was ordered to fall back at once from Warminster to Devizes. Churchill, Grafton and Berwick would accompany the King to London. Salisbury itself was all that day in an uproar, a prey to conflicting rumours and delayed decisions. At noon there arrived the news that Devonshire and Danby had declared for William and were in control of the North.

Feversham and Berwick went immediately to James, whose nose had started to bleed again, though with less violence than before. Berwick asked if they might speak to him privately and, when Dr Radcliffe had reluctantly withdrawn after their assurance that they would instantly recall him were he needed, both fell on their knees.

'What does this mean?' said the King. 'Get up.'

'You see us like this, sir,' said Feversham, 'that we may add force to what we ask.'

'Father,' said Berwick, 'for God's sake put my uncle Churchill under arrest before it is too late.'

'You have proof?'

'Was not his advice at the Council yesterday proof enough?'

'He may have been honest in his opinion. We are all soldiers and know well enough how minds may vary on a strategy.'

Berwick could not control his impatience. 'I know your feeling on this, James,' the King said quietly; 'but you must see mine. John Churchill was my faithful friend before you were born. Everything he has he owes to me. He is tied by twenty years.'

'I've known him as long as you, sir,' said Feversham, 'but I've never known him tied by anything but his own interest.'

They argued for an hour. At the end of it, a servant came with news that the Lieutenant-General Churchill urgently desired to speak with the King and the Commander-in-Chief.

'Admit him,' said James.

Churchill reported that Kirke had refused to obey the order to fall back to Devizes.

'What reason does he give?'

'That the order was improperly countersigned and that your Majesty, having been unable to visit him at Warminster, has been misled as to the true situation.'

'You will arrest him at once, sir?' said Feversham.

'Of course,' James answered.

'Shall I ride over to bring him back?' suggested Churchill.

'No,' said the King, 'at such a time as this I should prefer you within call here. Lord Feversham will see to it.'

Churchill did not desert until the King had gone to bed. Then, with Grafton and some others, he rode over to Axminster. When he arrived, Schomberg, mercenary soldier as he was, refused his hand and said: 'You are the first deserter of the rank of Lieutenant-General that I have ever known.' But William welcomed him with open arms.

IX

The King was breakfasting with George of Denmark when Churchill's letter was brought to him. He read it twice to make certain that he understood its import—that Churchill, while admitting that he owed everything to James, was impelled to yield to a paramount duty. As a good Protestant, he could not in conscience draw his sword against the Protestant cause, etc. etc. . . .

He passed the letter to his son-in-law to read. George had

in recent days acquired almost the status of court-jester. His catch-phrase of 'Est-il possible?' had been used, unvarying in its inflection, as every new desertion or piece of bad news had been announced. Now he invested it with a passionate anger which made James feel almost affectionate towards him. The King could not have been expected to understand that George was genuinely indignant and surprised that Churchill had gone without telling him and so had ruined the original plan that they should all go together.

James left the rest of his breakfast untouched and went to his room, giving orders that Feversham and Berwick should attend him there. He saw by their faces that they had already heard the news.

'I owe you both an apology,' he said. 'You were right in your estimate of this—this person. I should have arrested him and his associates as you asked me. Now we must lose no time in getting back to London, for we cannot depend on the troops. They will have been corrupted by these—these traitors.'

'You wrong the men,' said Berwick. 'They are loyal enough. It is only the officers who are sold to William.'

But the blow was too severe for James to believe longer in any loyalty. 'No,' he said, 'let us lose no time in setting out.'

As the morning wore on, the burden on James's spirit grew heavier. He was incapable of thinking of anything else. During the last fortnight he had become accustomed to treachery as a political force to be reckoned with, but until now it had never invaded his private kingdom. Looking back to Cornbury, those centuries ago, he would have welcomed

a repetition of that shock as a relief, a mere dream of discomfort compared with this waking misery. He had nothing
in his own experience to match it against and, to ease his
anger, fell back on analogies. Like his father, he was an
admirer of the playwright, Shakespeare. There was a
moment in *Henry V* where the King had discovered the
treachery of his friend:

> What shall I say to thee, Lord Scroop? thou cruel,
> Ingrateful, savage and inhuman creature!
> Thou that didst bear the key to all my counsels,
> Thou knewst the very bottom of my soul
> That almost mights't have coined me into gold
> Woulds't thou have practised on me for thy use—
> May it be possible that foreign hire
> Could out of thee extract one spark of evil?

James could not remember the passage exactly, but phrases
were there . . . 'didst bear the key to all my counsels' . . .
'knewst my soul' . . . 'Foreign hire' . . . But even Scroop
was not hypocrite enough to put it on the basis of religion . . .

If John Churchill could do this, coldly, after repeated
protestations of loyalty, what of the rest? What, above all,
of Sarah Churchill? Was it possible that the infection might
spread to his daughter's household? He would not for the
world have Anne imperilled. If he had been foolish in his
trust before, he would make up for it by swift action now.
He wrote to the Queen asking her to arrest Lady Churchill
immediately and sent it 'haste, haste, post-haste' to Whitehall
by his special courier.

On the march to Andover he kept George of Denmark by him and, for once, found his stupidity restful.

X

On Sunday, November 25, the King and those still faithful to him remained at Andover. He had given Berwick command of Churchill's regiment and, for the moment, refused to allow him to return to Portsmouth. He needed him too badly. Yet Portsmouth and the safety of the Prince of Wales was the thought now which overtopped all others. To the Admiral, Lord Dartmouth, he wrote an urgent, emphatic letter: ' 'Tis my son they aim at and 'tis my son I must endeavour to preserve, whatever becomes of me; therefore I conjure you to assist Lord Dover in getting him sent away in yachts as soon as wind and weather will permit for the first port they can get to in France, and that with as much secrecy as may be; and see that trusty men be put in the yachts that he may be exposed to no other danger than that of the sea; and know I shall look upon this as one of the greatest pieces of service you can do me.'

He entrusted the letter with additional verbal instructions to Lord Dover whom, at the same time, he officially appointed Commander-in-Chief at Portsmouth in Berwick's absence. Harry Jermyn, Baron Dover, little of body, large of head and short of leg was, like Feversham, one of James's oldest and most trusted friends. All three were of an age and, in their twenties, had campaigned together on the Continent. Harry Jermyn, too, it was said, had been a little in love with James's first wife—but now that was a bond

G

rather than a barrier. He had trusted Harry then and could trust him now.

As soon as Dover had set off down the Portsmouth road —hurried away almost before he had time to finish his breakfast—James sent an equerry to find George of Denmark, whom he wanted to consult further about possible changes in Anne's household. The equerry was unable to find him. Eventually, a letter was discovered and brought to James. It began in the usual manner, though it was rather more flowery than previous missives and was obviously not George's unaided work: 'My just concern for that religion in which I have been so happily educated, which my judgment truly convinced me to be the best and for the support whereof I am highly interested in my native country—and was not England then become so by the most endearing tie? . . .'

James did not trouble to read further but asked curtly: 'Who went with the Prince of Denmark?' Feversham told him Ormond and Drumlanrig, Queensberry's son. But he did not seem to hear them; and Berwick noticed that he was actually smiling. For a moment he was apprehensive for his father's self-control. There was no need. James had suddenly remembered his brother Charles's estimate of the Prince of Denmark and echoes of the dead, gay voice comforted him: 'I have tried George drunk and I have tried him sober and there is nothing in him.'

'So little *Est-il possible?* has gone too, has he?' said James to Berwick. 'After all a good trooper would have been a greater loss.'

'Even an indifferent trooper!' answered Berwick.

James suddenly became hard again: 'Except that he is Anne's husband! Poor Anne! It will hurt the child so.'

At the Cockpit they were making final preparations for flight. Anne was copying out the letter which Compton had composed for her. Churchill's messenger had, for safety, mentioned no one by name; but they assumed that the original plan had been carried out and that Churchill, Grafton and the Prince of Denmark had all deserted together. The letter was addressed to the Queen: 'Madam, I beg your pardon if I am so deeply affected with the surprising news of the Prince's being gone as not to be able to see you, but to leave this paper to express my humble duty to the King and yourself; and to let you know that I am gone to absent myself to avoid the King's displeasures, which I am not able to bear, either against the Prince or myself. And I shall stay at so great a distance as not to return before I hear the happy news of a reconcilement: and, as I am confident the Prince did not leave the King with any other design than to use all possible means for his preservation, so I hope you will do me the justice to believe that I am incapable of following him for any other end. . . .'

'But we're not actually going to William, are we?' said Anne, at this point.

'Not immediately,' said Compton, 'we're going to Nottingham to join Devonshire and the others. But that phrase is correct enough. And it will look better in print.'

'What print?'

'I've arranged with our presses that a copy of your letter will be sold on the streets tomorrow morning.'

'Why?'

'Because,' intervened Sarah Churchill, 'all London will know you're gone, so all London must know *where* you've gone and *why* you've gone. I did tell you, you remember.'

'Yes, Sarah; but all this excitement makes me forget things.'

Outside there was the sudden sound of horses and a coach stopping. The Bishop, looking cautiously from behind the curtains, went white. 'The Queen,' he said. 'Why has she come here?'

'She often comes to visit me, as you know,' said Anne. 'But you must go at once, my Lord. You can be the first to use the new back-stairs we've had made for tonight. They only finished them this morning!' But Compton and Lady Churchill were already out of the room before Anne had finished the sentence.

By the time that Mary Beatrice was ushered in, Anne was quietly reading a volume of Bishop Ken's sermons, attended by Mrs Danvers, who, ignorant of the plot, was invaluable for her innocence.

The Queen came straight to the point. Having told Anne to dismiss the Lady-in-Waiting, she informed her that she had received orders from the King to put Lady Churchill under arrest, since her husband had deserted to William. The Lord Chamberlain with a guard were waiting outside, so that there should be no scandal.

Anne burst into genuine tears.

The sight distressed the Queen. The childishness made her think of Anne as she had first known her—a smiling little girl of eight welcoming her, not quite fifteen, less as a stepmother than as 'the new playmate' that James had called her. After a moment's doubt, Anne had come straight up to her and kissed her and presented her with the large and somewhat dirty doll which had been her favourite . . .

'Anne dear,' said Mary Beatrice. 'I understand how you must feel. Perhaps you did not know that Lord Churchill was a traitor. The news only arrived last night.'

'I—I can't believe it,' sobbed Anne.

'It is hard for any of us to,' said Mary Beatrice, 'but it is true, nevertheless. He was an absolute Judas. Worse than Judas for he owes everything he has to your father, who picked him out of the dirt.'

'But what he has done, wicked as it is, is nothing to do with Sarah! You can't blame her.'

'We may hope so; but to leave her here is a risk which, because of his love for you, the King dare not take. The traitors must not be in a position to harm you.'

'But, little mother'—Anne judged that the childhood phrase might not be without effect—'not *now;* not at this moment. It's all too sudden. Tomorrow. If it must be, let it wait till tomorrow. There can be no harm in that. And it would be kind to all of us. If you love me at all——'

'You know I do, my pet, but this is a matter of state.'

Desperately Anne argued and pleaded and sobbed until at last after nearly an hour she gained her point and was able to watch Mary Beatrice drive away, having postponed the arrest until Monday morning.

When the Queen had gone, Anne called Mrs Danvers back and told her that the Royal visit had made her feel indisposed and that she was retiring to bed and did not want to be disturbed in the morning until she rang. As soon as she was safely alone in her room with the door locked upon Mrs Danvers (who, as usual, lay in the antechamber) Sarah Churchill and Lady Fitzharding—the sister of William of Orange's Elizabeth Villiers—came into her by the newly-constructed back-stairs which led from a private door in her room straight down into St James's Park. The women waited, talking in excited whispers, until the hour appointed by Compton, when they stole into the Park, and over a slough of wet November mud, reached the hackney-coach which the Bishop, disguised as a footman, had waiting for them.

Within less than half an hour they were safe in the official residence of the Bishops of London in Aldersgate Street, refreshing themselves while the present occupant of the see discarded his footman's livery for the buff coat and jack-boots which, with his broadsword and pistols, were the outward and visible sign that he was now a colonel, holding a commission from the Earl of Devonshire in Nottingham, whither he was deputed to take the Princess.

XI

'As I was walking in Westminster Hall,' recorded Lord Clarendon in his diary for Monday, November 26, 'on a sudden was a rumour all about the Princess was gone away, nobody knew whither: that somebody had violently carried her away. I went at once to the Cockpit. I found all the women in great consternation. All the light I could get was that, last night, after Her Royal Highness was in bed, the chamber doors locked and Mrs Danvers in bed in the outer room, she rose again, went down the back-stairs and accompanied only by Lady Churchill and two others, went into a coach and six horses, which stood ready at the street gate. This was all I could learn.'

Though it was not accurate in all particulars, it was Truth itself compared with the rumours accidentally or deliberately disseminated throughout London. As soon as Anne's disappearance had been discovered, her servants had run to the Palace screaming that the Popish priests had murdered their mistress and taken away the body. Her old nurse, Mrs Buss, demanded to see the Queen and asked her, in her rudest manner, what she had done with her. Mary Beatrice, suddenly realizing the meaning of the scene on the previous afternoon, retorted: 'I suppose your mistress is where she wants to be, but I assure you that I know nothing about it. We shall hear of her again very soon, I am certain.'

Thereafter the women redoubled their efforts. Aided now by Lady Clarendon, they rushed round the palace shouting that the Papists had murdered her and that all good Protestants had better look to themselves since she, who was the only prop of Protestantism, was gone. All the Queen's servants they met, they asked: 'What have you done with our mistress's body?'

The news spread quickly to the streets, where the mob shouted accusations against Mary Beatrice and threatened her with death. The rumours magnified and 'considering the ferment people were in and how susceptible they were of an ill impression against the Queen, might have caused her to be torn to pieces by the rabble.' When the hubbub was at its height, however, the news of George of Denmark's desertion arrived in London and gradually the more sober element began to see a connection between the flight of the husband and the flight of the wife.

The bleak November light had faded before James arrived back in the capital. It was just after five when he reached Whitehall and he had already heard the news about Anne shouted in the streets. When Mary Beatrice confirmed that it was true, he said: 'God help me! My own children have forsaken me!' Those round him, watching his strained, strange face, feared for his reason—a Lear with only a Regan and a Goneril. But this time the King did not think of the playwright but of the Psalmist and they heard him mutter over and over again: 'O, if my enemies only had cursed me, I could have borne it; but it was thou—thou—mine own . . .'

At last the tension broke and he started to cry.

XIX

Debate

NEXT day all the Lords of the Council who were still in London met the King at Whitehall. James reminded them that, on the eve of his departure for Salisbury, a petition had been presented to him by the bishops and some of the temporal peers that he should summon Parliament. This he had promised to do as soon as circumstances made it possible. He had not then imagined that the officers of his army were disloyal. Their defection had altered the situation completely. What, in the opinion of the Council, was the best course of action?

Halifax, Godolphin and Jeffreys all insisted that, as a first measure, Parliament must immediately be called. There was now no hope for the Throne or the country except through the assembly of the representatives of the country. Pending the opening of Parliament, which, inevitably, would take some weeks, it might be advisable to open negotiations with the Prince of Orange.

Then Clarendon spoke. Having already made his arrangements to join William, he felt that he could at last give vent to the feelings he had so long and so successfully concealed. Even the King's most pertinacious political opponents were shocked by 'the indecency and insolence' of his attack. Addressing the King 'as pedagogue to pupil,' he started an invective against Popery which might have been taken verbatim from one of the gutter-pamphlets; he blamed the King's policy of toleration for all the evils that had befallen the country; the crowning folly, he said, was allowing Catholics in the army; even at this moment, a Catholic regiment was being raised in London, into which all the French tradesmen in town were admitted and from which Protestants were carefully excluded. . . .

James, remembering the Clarendon of ten days ago apparently broken-hearted at his son's treachery, was too taken aback to interrupt him until this lie made it imperative.

'That is not true,' he said.

'I have been so informed on good authority, sir.'

'You have been misinformed.'

The rebuke was a spur. Clarendon went on to accuse the King of personal cowardice. Why did he retreat from Salisbury? Could people be blamed for submitting to the invader when they saw their King run away at the head of the army?

He was interrupted again, but this time by Halifax who, with a tact which some thought flattery, brought the conversation back to an impersonal level. But what he had to say, despite its delicate saying, had no comfort in it. The King would be advised to make certain concessions to popular feeling. He should at once dismiss all Catholics from office; he should sever his diplomatic connection with France and openly renounce his friendship with Louis; and he should pardon, without exception, all deserters.

'All deserters?' said James. 'I cannot do it.'

'It would be wise to pardon where you cannot punish,' said Halifax.

'Not Churchill,' said James. 'I must make an example of Churchill, whom I raised so high from nothing. And he alone is to blame for this. That has become clear to me at last. He has corrupted my army. He has corrupted my child. He would have sold me to the Prince of Orange but for God's special providence. My Lords, you are strangely anxious for the safety of traitors. None of you troubles himself about the safety of the Crown.'

'Sir,' said Halifax, 'you must believe that it is the King's safety which is our one care. But, as things are, there are only two ways of securing it. Either you must conquer or you must conciliate. If your Majesty, after all that has happened, has still any hope of safety in arms, we have nothing more to say; but if not, you can only be safe by granting what, rightly or wrongly, your people ask of you.'

'My lords,' said James, 'you have spoken with great freedom, and I thank you for it. On one point I have already made up my mind. I shall call a Parliament. The other suggestions which have been offered are of grave importance and you will not be surprised if I take a night to reflect on them before I decide.'

William's army was advancing rapidly. News from the North that Danby had offered the Governor of Hull 'five thousand pounds to be paid to you a month after it is done' for the surrender of the city and that the offer had been promptly accepted had heartened him considerably, since there was now less need of pretence. His mercenaries among which discipline had been very strict for fear of alienating the English, were also fortunate in finding legitimate occasions for amusement at the Catholic churches they managed to discover. At one of them, after carefully desecrating it, they broke the sanctuary lamp, stole the sanctus bell, drank uproariously out of the chalice to annoy the priest and finally dressed the inevitable cat in the eucharistic vestments and solemnly burnt it 'on the top of a bonfire.'

When Clarendon arrived at the Dutch headquarters, he was welcomed effusively by William who assured him that he would never forget such a 'seasonable service' as Cornbury's coming over to him—a point which Bentinck emphasized later and which the gratified father noted in his diary: 'He made me many compliments upon my son's so early going to the Prince, of which, he said, the Prince was very sensible.'

He found Churchill full of questions, of which the first was the day on which Anne left the Cockpit. Clarendon told him.

'I am surprised,' answered Churchill, 'that she left it so late.'

Clarendon countered with another question. What was the truth about the plan, which the King had told him, of delivering James to William if he had gone to inspect the outposts at Warminster and from which only a providential recurrence of the nose-bleeding had saved him?

Churchill gave that frank open smile of his, tinged with a pained amusement: 'A most absolute lie! How could anyone believe it of me? I would die for His Majesty and I left

him only because my religion was in danger from his mis-
guided tyranny. For which reason, my Lord, I conclude
that you also have come here?'

There was nothing more to say.

Clarendon's greeting with Dr Burnet had in it that
particular overtone of emotion which he reserved for
Anglican dignitaries and it was disconcerting that when he
told him that James had consented to call Parliament, the
Doctor went apoplectic with anger and shouted: 'A
Parliament? A free Parliament? It's impossible. There can be
no Parliament. There *must* be no Parliament. It's impossible!'

James appointed Halifax and Godolphin as his Commissioners to William, adding to them Daniel Finch, Earl
of Nottingham, who held a unique position in politics.
Though early involved with Shrewsbury and his co-
conspirators, Nottingham had refused to sign the invitation
to William and he had remained trusted by the one side but
loyal to the other. 'By a delicacy of honour in all points,' as
a contemporary noted, 'he preserved his respect to the King
by not quitting him and his friends by not betraying them.'

The three took down to Hungerford, which William had
now made his headquarters, the formal note: 'Sir, the King
commandeth us to acquaint you that he observeth all the
differences and causes of complaint alleged by Your Highness
seem to be referred to a free Parliament. His Majesty, as he
hath already declared, was resolved before this to call one,
but thought that in the present state of affairs it was advisable
to defer it till things were more composed. Yet, seeing that
his people still continue to desire it, he hath put forth his

proclamation in order to it and hath issued forth his writs for the calling of it. And to prevent any cause of interruption in it, he will consent to everything that can be reasonably required for the security of all that shall come to it.

'His Majesty hath therefore sent us to attend Your Highness for the adjusting of all matters that shall be agreed to be necessary for the freedom of election and the security of sitting, and is ready to enter immediately into a treaty in order to it.

'His Majesty proposeth that in the meantime the respective armies may be restrained within such limits, and at such a distance from London, as may prevent the apprehensions that the Parliament may in any way be disturbed, being desirous that the meeting of it may be no longer delayed than must be by the usual and necessary forms.'

When the three Commissioners arrived, Zuylestein announced laughingly to his fellow-Dutchmen that the King had sent to capitulate; but, William, taking the document and the accompanying formal note, written by James's secretary in French, the language of diplomacy, suddenly, for the first and last time, hesitated. Slowly, and as if the words were forced from him, he said: 'This is the first letter I have ever received from my uncle which was not written in his own hand and in English.'

But the moment of vision in which William saw the paper as, as it were, a bill of account for his ambition, quickly passed. His schemer's mind returned to the document and instantly fixed on the flaw. He must, of course, keep his declared word about calling Parliament; but it must be his Parliament not James's. At the moment, the country as a whole would undoubtedly be loyal to the King. Fortunately the words 'he will consent to everything that can be reasonably required' could be stretched to ensure impossibility. He would demand that as a preliminary to Parliament all Catholics should be dismissed from their posts; that James should recognize the justice of William's cause; that Portsmouth should be surrendered to prevent a possible invasion by the French; that James should maintain the cost of William's army; and that, when Parliament, after these precautions, met, the first thing it should do was to examine the proofs of the Prince of Wales's legitimacy.

William calculated that James, rather than agree to terms which would make him a bad Catholic, a bad sovereign, a bad soldier, a bad administrator and a bad father, would choose to abdicate. After that, a 'free Parliament' could be summoned with safety.

XX

The Prince leaves Portsmouth

JAMES'S one preoccupation now was to secure the safety of his wife and child. The nightmares of his own boyhood, when his father's care had been to get his mother, his brother and himself safely to France, entered and mingled with his dreams, so that he would wake from fitful sleep with a start thinking he was his father on the scaffold. And, waking, he could still see the identity of situation. Once Mary Beatrice and the Prince of Wales were safe under the protection of Louis XIV, he could turn with an easier heart to die for his kingship and his faith.

From France had come already unofficial help. The fiery little Comte de Lauzun, whose Gascon spirit was ignited by danger, had with his friend St Victor (whose father's life James years ago had saved in battle), come over as knight-errants from Paris to offer their swords to England. To them James could, with confidence, entrust the Queen and the heir of England. At eleven o'clock on the night of Sunday, December 2, they came to him secretly to make their final plans. Next day they decided to ride to Portsmouth with the Queen, disguised as an Italian seamstress, to board there the Royal yacht, *The Mary* (named in happier days like its sister yacht, *The Anne*, after the King's daughter), where the Prince and his nurse, with Lady Powis, would have been taken aboard earlier by Lord Dover. Lord Dartmouth, whose letter James was hourly expecting, would see that the fleet ensured, as far as possible, the safety of *The Mary's* passage into the Channel.

Mary Beatrice, when James told her of the plan, flatly refused to go.

'Nothing, James, nothing,' she said, 'will induce me to leave you again. As things are here now——'

'But, sweetheart,' said James, 'the safety of the boy——'

'I understand that. You can send the boy to France or wherever you think most secure for him, but I shall stay here with you.'

'You would not wish to be separated from the boy.'

'I do not pretend I should like it, but I could bear it with patience. What I could not bear at all would be to be separated from you. I will never go through anything like those ten days again.'

'But there is no telling what may happen.'

'No,' she said, 'but I am prepared for the worst that can be imagined. Even prison, if you are there with me, would be better than the greatest ease and security in the world without you.'

In vain he tried to shake her; but neither pleas nor orders would move her. At last, when he fell silent because there was nothing left to say, she asked: 'Will you come to France too?'

'Not as long as there is any chance left to fight in England.'

'But if there is not?'

'I had not thought of such a thing happening. Why?'

'Because if you follow me, then I will go.'

'But, sweetheart, even for you I could not be a coward.'

She knew that well enough and had not meant it that way.

'I should never ask you to be. But if you have no army, you cannot fight. And it is not courage to allow yourself to be taken prisoner by William. From France you could rally those who remain loyal, get Louis's help and come back to take the Kingdom again.'

'If it came to it——'

'That is all I say, all I ask. If it came to it, will you follow me?'

He still hesitated for minutes that seemed to her hours. She was content that it should be so and stood quite still, waiting for the word which she knew he would keep.

'If I am alive, sweetheart, I will follow you as soon as I can.'

'Then I will go with Lauzun to Portsmouth tomorrow. Now let us go to bed. It is very late.'

The morrow, however, brought news which prevented her from going to Portsmouth. The long-expected letter from Lord Dartmouth arrived. The Admiral refused to assist James in facilitating the Prince's escape. His reason was plain enough: to send the Prince of Wales out of the country into the hands of a foreign power was not only high treason, but it was an act which could be construed to the King's disadvantage. 'I most humbly hope you will no longer

entertain,' he concluded, 'so much as a thought of doing
that which will give your enemies an advantage, though
never so falsely grounded, to distrust your son's just right,
which you have asserted and manifested to the world, in
the matter of his being your real son, born of the Queen.
Pardon me, therefore, if on my bended knees I beg of you
to apply yourself to other counsels, for doing this looks like
nothing less than despair, to the degree of not only giving
your enemies encouragement but distrust of your friends
and people, who I do not despair will yet stand by you in
the defence and right of your lawful successor.' Dartmouth
ended by begging him to give orders for the Prince's
immediate return to London lest the troops of the Prince of
Orange should bar the way between Portsmouth and the
capital.

By the same courier from Portsmouth, James received
news that the loyalty of the navy was uncertain and that the
sailors wished him to open negotiations with the Prince of
Orange. This was an even heavier blow than the defection
of the army for the sailor-king, who had 'encouraged,
cherished and promoted that profession more than any King
since the Conquest; who had been all his life a model and
example as well as a spectator and praiser of their courage;
who had gloried in nothing so much as that he had shared
with them in the hardships and dangers of defending the
dominion of the seas.' A courtier, watching him as he
received the news, remarked: 'The poor King is mightily
broken; a great heart can't so easily bend.'

In the shock of that moment, it was pardonable that
James did not connect the two pieces of news and realize

that Dartmouth's letter was the result of the other happenings. He did not, even then, question Dartmouth's loyalty, though he critized his judgment; but it was not until months later that he understood the brilliance of the letter. Dartmouth had discovered that several naval officers who were in William's pay had planned to intercept *The Mary* as soon as it was out of sight of Portsmouth, capture the Prince and deliver him to William. He dared not write to warn James of this, lest his letter should be intercepted. He was not in a strong enough position to arrest the officers, lest the whole navy should mutiny. He therefore said the one thing which he hoped would make James at least change his plans and fetch back the Prince from Portsmouth to the comparative safety of London.

James understood at least that no time must be lost in ordering that. He sent a courier to Lord and Lady Powis commanding them to bring back the Prince at once to the capital and he made what arrangements he could for their safe-conduct. In this extremity, with neither fleet nor army reliable, it seemed to him that he dared trust none but Catholics, and he was forced at last to make that discrimination he had so long and carefully resisted. He sent two Catholic regiments of horse to march to Portsmouth, accompanied by a detachment of Irish dragoons, to bring home the Prince of Wales.

In Portsmouth itself, however, Lord Dover and the Powises, advised by Dartmouth, judged it too dangerous to wait until these troops arrived. Dover told the loyal Colonel Clifford to be ready by six o'clock the next morning to provide an escort for the Royal coach; but during the night he was seized with panic and changed the hour to five, so that the fugitives could be at least three miles clear of the town before daybreak. Clifford was to ride at full speed to overtake the coach, which contained Dover, Lord and Lady Powis, the nurse and the baby and which was attended only by Captain Macarthy, an Irish officer, who refused to leave them.

Clifford and the escort had still not overtaken them by the time they reached Bere Forest. At the edge of that twenty-five miles of woodland and heath north of the Portsdown Hills they stopped. Here, if anywhere, William's men would try to ambush them. It would have been folly to go on unattended. Macarthy started to ride back to find Clifford and explain the urgency; but before he was out of sight of the coach he met an old forest dweller.

'Would you be having any news hereabouts, my honest fellow?' he asked him.

'News? We've no news here in the Forest, unless it's news that I've lost ten pigs.'

'They'd have been stolen, likely?'

'No, sir, we're honest men, we foresters. None'd steal from the other. We'd know our own too soon.'

'But those who pass through the Forest—soldiers, it may be, marauding and stealing? You've seen no soldiers here lately.'

'Yes, Colonel Norton's boys, they be about here; that I do know. But they'd not steal. They're honest and god-fearing are Colonel Norton's. The great Dick Norton he is, one of Cromwell's men—but you'd be too young to mind him. He'd hang anyone who stole.'

'And the good, godfearing Colonel—and may he be praised for his honesty—he's about here with his men, is he?'

'Well, he was staying here last night; but he wouldn't want my pigs, would he?'

'No, come to think of it now, he wouldn't. And may you find them safely! But, before you go seeking them, will you tell me if there's a road to London beside the one that goes through the Forest? It's muddy and wet here for a coach; and I've got some ladies in it——'

'The Forest way's no way for a coach. Why, with this weather we've been having, you'd get bogged up before ever you got clear of it. No, you want to take the other road round it. Go back to the crossroads there and bear north. It's a good road, that one is. Runs up to Petersfield.'

Macarthy thanked the old man and returned to the coach. There was no question now of waiting for the escort. They turned and drove as fast as they could along the road skirting the Forest, while on the road through it Norton, with two captains, two lieutenants and a hundred picked horse, waited to intercept them. William had so ordered it, having been told by his spies in Portsmouth of the intended escape.

The guards and dragoons who had been sent to meet the Prince found him at Guildford and after a rest, the cavalcade made its way at a more leisurely pace to the outskirts of London. Before entering, they divided again. The soldiers made their return from the south, alone. They found that the precaution had been necessary. As they were known to be Catholic regiments, an enormous rabble was waiting for them, armed with sticks and stones. Unable even to defend themselves without actually counter-attacking the mob, they were forced to disband. But the Prince, wrapped now for additional safety in the cloak of St Victor, who had accompanied the troops to Guildford, entered from the north and was met at Knightsbridge by the Household troops which James, from Whitehall, had sent to wait for him.

XXI

The Flight of the Queen

THE London mob, that Sunday evening, determined to enjoy itself. It broke into the Jesuits' chapel and, piling all the wainscoting and the seats in the middle, set light to them. While the chapel was burning, some dressed themselves in the vestments; others lighted the candles in the great gilt candlesticks and a procession was formed, led by a contingent with oranges on swords and sticks. They marched victoriously by a regiment of guards standing in disciplined formation, to the Spanish Embassy. This they proceeded to beseige. Though the Ambassador managed to escape with his life, they plundered all his furniture, plate, money and three coaches, destroyed his library and all his papers and made away with £500,000 which had been entrusted to the Embassy for safe-custody as well as the plate of James's own chapel. Then they made another bonfire, whose 'wonderful light' frightened many citizens into thinking it the start of another Fire of London.

At Whitehall, James and Mary Beatrice watched the flames reddening the sky and listened to the yells and cat-calls in the street. Then, with an appearance of unconcern, they supped at the usual time and retired to bed at ten o'clock.

As soon as the palace was quiet and at rest, they rose again and dressed. At midnight St Victor, dressed as a common seaman, came into James's apartment by a secret door, bringing with him the dress which the Queen was to wear. While she was changing, he and Lauzun went down to wait in Madame de Labadie's rooms where the Prince of Wales was ready with his nurse. Everything had been prepared for the escape. Earlier in the day, Francesco Riva, the Keeper of the Queen's Wardrobe, had hired two private yachts at Gravesend, one in the name of Lauzun, the other in that of the Countess Vittoria Davia, the tall, witty childhood friend of the Queen, whose laundress Mary Beatrice was to pretend to be. The Countess, with her brother, Lord and Lady Powis, Sir William Waldegrave, the Prince's physician, Father Gallie, the Queen's confessor and some other faithful attendants, were already on one of the yachts, awaiting their arrival.

When at last James and Mary Beatrice, having made their farewells, came into the room, the King could hardly speak. His voice, usually so steady, trembled as he said to Lauzun: 'I confide my wife and my son to your care. At all costs, get them quickly to France.' Lauzun bowed and gave his hand to the Queen to lead her away. She looked back once at James, but neither trusted themselves to speak.

The party went by way of the Stone Gallery and down the back-stairs into the privy-garden. The coach of the Florentine envoy, which St Victor had borrowed, was waiting at the gate. On the way out they had to pass six sentinels, who challenged with the usual: Who goes there? but, on being answered: A friend and observing that St Victor had the master-key of all the doors and gates, made no attempt to stop them. The Queen, with the Prince, his two nurses and Lauzun, got into the coach, but St Victor insisted on sitting beside the coachman to see that he drove by the shortest way to the Horse Ferry, where he had ordered a boat to wait for him. For the last few nights, he had accustomed the boatmen to row him across the river under pretence of a sporting expedition, taking with him some cold provisions and a gun to give colour to it; but as it was now three in the morning, pitch dark, and stormy, St Victor feared that the excuse was unlikely to pass muster. But money persuaded the boatmen to transport them across the flooded river rendered the more dangerous—as St Victor recorded it—'by the violence of the wind and the heavy and incessant rain,' and they landed safely at Lambeth Stairs. Here Dominic Dufour, the King's page, and Francesco Riva were waiting for them, but the coach and six, which Lauzun had ordered to be there, was still in the yard of the Swan Inn. St Victor ran to the Swan to hasten the coachman, while the Queen, with the Prince in her arms, took what shelter she could against the tower of St Mary's Church. Her eyes strained across the river to the lights still burning in Whitehall, as she tried to identify the room where James would be sitting alone.

At the inn St Victor's idiom and accent had aroused suspicion which was increased by the sight of a coach and six waiting in the storm at that hour in the morning. The watchman, with a lantern, started towards the churchyard to investigate. Riva deliberately tripped him, fell down in the mud with him to make it appear a blundering accident and, while making profuse apologies, surreptitiously ex-

tinguished his lantern. He then helped the watchman to his
feet and set him on his way back to the inn, unlighted, to
dry himself.

Meanwhile St Victor had got the coach to start and the
party was soon on the way to Gravesend. The only danger
they encountered was a company of guards who called out:
'Let's have a look: here's a carriage full of papists,' but for
some reason or other they did not carry out their threat.
'God willed it so that they changed their purpose, for no
one came near us.' With the country lanes deep in mud,
the twenty miles to Gravesend took longer than had been
allowed for and, as dawn had broken before they reached it,
three Irish captains, whom the King had sent as being
especially trustworthy, put off from the yacht in a small
boat, and, hugging the shore, rowed to meet the fugitives.
They waited for them a little to the west of the town, and
when at last they arrived, they rowed the Queen straight
to the yacht. As the master of it, whose name was Gray, had
no suspicion of the identity of his belated passenger, it was
essential to sustain the acted part. Mary Beatrice, going
aboard, carried the Prince under her arm, carefully packed
up to represent a bundle of linen and Vittoria Davia was
loud in her reproaches to the laundress for keeping them all
waiting.

As soon as the yacht weighed anchor, St Victor rode back
on the King's fastest horse, which had been provided for him,
to give James the news.

James thanked him and said: 'Now that the Queen and
the Prince are safe, I can die at the head of my army.'

XXII

Decision

THE heroic moment was forbidden. Facing the situation as it was in the uncomprising light of that December morning, James realized that he could not fight. For one thing, he was still in negotiation with William who, estimating that time was on his side, had resolved on the tactics of delay and was interminably protracting the proceedings at Hungerford. James could not therefore resort to arms without breaking faith. More importantly, he could not involve his subjects in another civil war. When he had ridden to Salisbury, three weeks ago, it was to swiftly crush a rebellion. Now, with a handful of officers and leaderless troops, any action would involve a long struggle of which no man could see the end.

Yet the change in circumstances did not affect the principle of his kingship, for which he was prepared to die as his father had died, even though he was not prepared to involve others in death. The problem that hammered at his brain was how, without blood-guiltiness, he could still fulfil his trust.

At last he saw a way through the maze. In his Accession Speech, he had promised: 'I shall make it my endeavour to preserve this Government both in Church and State as it is now by law established,' and he had kept his word. He, like his father, had resisted to the uttermost the attempts of the wealthy to bend the Constitution to their own ends by endeavouring to eliminate the reality of the Crown. When their fathers had triumphed over his father, the scaffold in Whitehall had nullified their victory by destroying their pretences. None had claimed or could claim that the Cromwellian interlude was anything but a military usurpation which, in due course drowned in its own anarchy, left the Kingship untouched and uncompromised to return to the murdered king's son. Now James, without dying, must effect the same thing. Though he himself lived, Kingship in England must publicly die until he or his son could reanimate it. William must be defined as a military usurper on the Cromwellian pattern and his possible reign as no true rule. James would suspend all government, join the Queen and the Prince in France and, in due course, return with an army to those parts of his kingdom—Scotland or Ireland— which still remained free.

And the means for this dramatic stroke, once he had taken the decision, were simple enough. None but the King could raise and command an army. None but the King, by his writ, could summon Parliament. None but the King could appoint or receive Ambassadors. Only with the King's Great Seal—that 'pestiferous lump of metal' to which jurists attached an almost mystical significance—could any act of government be transacted. He would therefore disband the army, burn the writs he had prepared for the summoning of Parliament and take the Great Seal with him in his flight.

He wrote to Feversham: 'Things being come to that extremity that I have been forced to send away the Queen and my son, the Prince of Wales, that they might not fall into my enemy's hands which they must have done had they stayed, I am obliged to do the same thing and endeavour to secure myself the best I can, in the hope that it will please God, out of His infinite mercy to this unhappy nation, to touch their hearts with true loyalty and honour.

'If I could have relied on all my troops I might not have been put to the extremity I am in, and would at least have had one blow for it; but, though I know there are many loyal and brave men amongst you, yet you know you yourself, and several of the General Officers, told me it was no ways advisable to venture myself at their head.

'There remains nothing more for me to do but to thank you and all those officers and soldiers who have stuck to me and been truly loyal. I hope you will still have the same fidelity to me and, though I do not expect you should expose yourselves by resisting a foreign army and poisoned nation, yet I hope your former principles are so rooted in you that you will keep yourselves free from associations with such pernicious things.'

James then burnt the writs which had not yet been sent out and made out in legal form an instrument annulling those which had. To Terriesi, the Tuscan Envoy, he entrusted all his private papers and £3,500 to be forwarded to the Queen. Then, having made his more personal arrangements, he drove to Somerset House and spent the evening with his sister-in-law, Catherine of Braganza, the Queen-Dowager.

When he returned to Whitehall he went straight to his room and was surprised when the Gentleman of the Bed-chamber, the thirty-year-old Scot, Thomas Bruce, Earl of Ailesbury, suddenly fell on his knees and, with tears in his eyes, begged him not to think of flight.

'You should not listen to coffee-house gossip,' said James.

'For the love of God, sir,' retorted Ailesbury, 'why do you try to hide it from me? I know your horses are now actually waiting for you at Lambeth. I know you have chosen as your mount the horse I had the honour of giving you—Bay Ailesbury. I know that Sir Edward Hales is waiting to attend you and the other three who are going with you are your equerry Ralph Sheldon, Labadie, your page and Dick Smith, your groom. And yet you will not tell me——'

'My daughter has deserted me; and my army; and even that man whom I raised from nothing and heaped every favour on. If such people betray me, what can I expect from those I have done so little for? And would it be surprising if, after such treatment, I went away?'

'Sir, I and many others will stand by you to the last drop of our blood. We can raise a body of loyal horse in a hour or two.'

'What good would that do?'

'We could join the Princess Anne at Nottingham where there are many who would come to you the moment you showed yourself.'

'No, not there,' said James, decisively.

'Then to York?'

'The Earl of Danby is there in force.'

'In force, sir!' said Ailesbury scornfully. 'Why, the

moment they see us his broomsticks and whistail militia and some raw bubbles he has drawn in will all run away. And so we'll go to Scotland and there, I warrant you, sir, you'll be safe enough.'

James smiled, but shook his head.

'Then stay at least, sir,' implored Ailesbury, 'till your three Commissioners are finished at Hungerford.'

'I have reasons for pinning little faith to that.'

'It seems that all I can ask then, sir, is that you will give me your hand to kiss, since we shall not meet again.'

'My Lord,' said James, putting his hands on his shoulders and looking into his eyes, 'they have tried to persuade me that you were a traitor, but I would not believe them.'

'Never, sir. Never. That is a most filthy slander.'

'I am sure of it, but you will understand that it is difficult for me, since Lord Churchill went, to know whom to trust. I trust you, but, for your own good now, I tell you nothing. Then, in honesty, you will know nothing and are free to make your way as you will. Let us leave it that I hope to see you again and so refuse to say farewell.'

Ailesbury, in tears, retired to the Guard Room and James went into the Bedchamber. By custom, during the Queen's absence, a Lord of the Bedchamber slept on a pallet-bed in the room and on duty that night was the Duke of Northumberland, Grafton's younger brother, whose loyalty to his uncle was as notable as Grafton's treachery.

'George,' said James, 'you understand what to do.'

'Yes, uncle, whatever happens I am not to open the door till the usual time for the levee. Then I am free to do whatever seems best to me.'

'Yes.'

'You can trust me.'

'I know.'

'I hope it will atone a little for my brother Henry.'

Northumberland then helped the King to change into a suit of ordinary clothes, such as might be worn by any country gentleman, adjusted his plain black wig, laughed with him at the transformation it effected, and took farewell of him at the secret door, where Sir Edward Hales was waiting.

The King and Hales, leaving the Palace by the same way as the Queen had left twenty-four hours before, drove in a hackney-coach plying for hire to the Horse Ferry where they took oars for Vauxhall, which was, after the events of last night, considered safer than Lambeth.

But the King looked towards Lambeth Palace, where Archbishop Sancroft lay peacefully asleep, as, in mid-stream, he dropped the Great Seal of England into the Thames.

H

XXIII

Terror in London

THE King's judgment had not been at fault. By his last act he had, out of the weakness of defeat, forced the hidden truth, for a moment, on to the stage of history. The Council which was immediately set up at Guildhall was admitted, even by those who constituted it, to have no more legal foundation than any revolutionary tribunal. And at the head of it was William Sancroft, Archbishop of Canterbury. Its first action was officially to invite William to come to London to assume the Government; its second, to order Dartmouth to fraternize with the Dutch fleet and immediately to dismiss all Catholics from his own. So, in their proper characters, exhibiting by actions their desires and motives, the plotters stood pin-pointed for posterity. But they were powerless to control the mob which had been their instrument but was now their master.

The cry was 'Down with Popery!' still, but as there were few chapels left to burn, it was now hardly an excuse. Along the Strand, the houses of the wealthy were pillaged and wrecked under pretence of searching for hidden Papists; the foreign Embassies, which were thought to conceal richer prizes were gutted, and Barillon, in St James's Square, was

saved only by a detachment of guards for which he had
asked some days before. But the Embassy of the Catholic
Duke of Tuscany and the Protestant Elector Palatine after
they had been ransacked went impartially up in flames.

Gangs of roughs patrolled the Thames, stopping and
searching every boat and holding up the fleeing citizens to
ransom. The first hour of darkness was as bright as day,
while the underworld danced and drank, shouted 'No King!
No Law!' and discussed plans for a thorough pillage of the
city on the morrow.

In the morning, though the capital, in many places,
resembled nothing so much as a city after siege and sack,
there was no cessation of the mob's fervour. And, as the day
wore on, it was increased by news of the arrest of Jeffreys.

The Lord Chancellor had left Whitehall shortly after
James and gone down to Wapping to make arrangements
with the owner of a collier for transport to the Continent.
Though he had shaved off his prominent eyebrows and
dressed himself as a common seaman, he had the ill-fortune
to be recognized by an extortionate moneylender of the
neighbourhood whose methods of making loans to sailors
had once landed him in Court. Jeffreys had addressed him
personally at some length and he had never afterwards been
able to forget that voice and that face. When he saw and
heard them in the Red Cow at Wapping, he had his revenge,
and in a short time the inn was besieged by crowds offering
to tear Jeffreys to pieces. But the news spread quickly and
Jeffreys was saved by the arrival of two regiments of train-
bands with a coach, in which he was conducted to the Lord
Mayor.

The Lord Mayor thus confronted with the Lord Chancellor was so affected by the strangeness of the circumstances that he immediately had an apoplectic stroke, from which he did not recover. As 'being ill, he could not sign any warrant,' things came to a temporary halt during which Jeffreys, noticeably unconcerned, 'sat down and ate heartily.' Eventually the Williamite colonel who had assumed command of the Tower arrived to arrest him on a warrant for high treason signed by Sancroft and his colleagues.

Constitutional absurdity could go no further, but the promoters of propaganda had still one trick in store. William was now within easy reach of London and wished to ensure himself an unmistakable welcome as the restorer of order whatever might be thought of his claims to kingship. Consequently, on the evening of Wednesday, December 12, a party of rumour-spreaders, dressed as country yokels, appeared in London and within an hour, from Piccadilly to Whitechapel, the citizens learnt with alarm that the tens of thousands of Irish troops, who had been disbanded by Feversham, were marching on the capital and massacring every man, woman and child on the road. They intended to take the capital and to put every Protestant to the sword. Children would be tortured into murdering their parents. Babies would be stuck on pikes, according to the well-known habit of the Papist Irish. All the Protestant churches would be razed to the ground. . . .

In the middle of the night, the drums of the militia beat to arms. Every main street was barricaded and more than twenty thousand pikes and muskets stood on guard. Private houses and public places remained lighted and women and

children with what household goods they could carry were
prepared for instant flight. By two in the morning, London
was in a state of defence such as might have deterred any
approaching enemy, had there been one. So the citizens
remained till dawn, when they were informed by the scouts
that had been sent out that there was no one in sight for miles
except the vanguard of William's army.

The sobering anti-climax of the day that followed was
mitigated by one authentic piece of news. The King was
still in England. He had been captured in Kent.

XXIV

James in Kent

THE small coasting-vessel which was to take James to France was moored at Elmley Ferry, opposite the Isle of Sheppey. From Vauxhall, it was forty miles by the high road through Rochester, but for safety's sake, the party took a quieter road further south by Chislehurst and Maidstone and had an early breakfast at the Woolpack on Pennenden Heath. They reached the ferry about ten o'clock in the morning, boarded the hoy and sailed northward through the narrow channel of the Swale to the mouth of the Medway. As the gale which had been raging for the last thirty-six hours had not dropped and the boat was sailing dangerously as soon as she was out on the open sea, the captain ran in to Sheerness to take in more ballast. The delay lost the tide and the hoy could not be floated again till eleven at night.

Patrolling that north coast of Kent were gangs of sailors who had discovered a thriving new trade by imitating the looters on the Thames and stopping all outgoing ships in search of fleeing Papists. In due course, having heard that during the day well-dressed strangers had been seen in the town, sixty sailors came up to the hoy and boarded her just as she was starting to float. Their captain, sword in one hand, pistol in the other, ran down to the cabin where the King was sitting with Sir Edward Hales and Sheldon and told them that he was arresting them as suspected Catholics. He assumed that James was Hales's chaplain, and one of the sailors taking the cue called out: 'Why, the rogue's that devil Father Petre.'

'Are you, by God?' said the ringleader.

'No,' said James.

But two other sailors confirmed the first: 'That's him. I'd know him anywhere by his lean jaws.'

'Search the hatchet-faced old bastard,' yelled another, aiming a blow at James, which Sheldon intercepted.

To prevent things getting worse, Hales rapidly put fifty guineas into the ringleader's hand and promised him a hundred more if he would let him and his friends escape.

'I must take you to Faversham,' said the ringleader, 'that's my duty. But, once we're there, I'll see everything's all right. Trust me.'

Hales had no alternative, and the man suggested that, as his gang were a somewhat unruly lot and would probably try to rob him while he was ashore making arrangements, it would be wise to entrust their money and valuables to him for safe keeping.

'If the magistrate finds you free men and no Papists, they'll be returned to you. If they're our lawful prize, then we'll divide them equally,' he explained.

They handed over their watches and what money they had and the man gave them a receipt for them, written out carefully, with the captain of the hoy as witness. But

James did not reveal the gold locket round his neck, or his coronation ring and a diamond bodkin of Mary Beatrice's which, for safety, he had slipped in his drawers; nor did he hand over a pair of diamond buckles which he had in his pocket.

When the ringleader, carrying his booty, had left them, promising to be back in three hours to ensure their escape, the gang decided that there was probably some money or valuables left to find and at dawn a party came into the cabin and started to search them.

The procedure was not pleasant. 'They fell a-searching their pockets and, opening their breeches, felt all about in a very rude manner, and the more, because they found nothing.'* One of them, however, located the diamond bodkin and cried out in triumph: 'A Prize! I've found a prize!'

'No,' said James, 'you've made a mistake. I've got several things in my pocket, but there's no prize there. There are scissors, some small keys, and a tooth-pick case. Probably that's what you've felt.'

To test it, the man suddenly thrust his hand in the King's pocket and, finding the articles that James had mentioned, searched no further. The diamond buckles which he found in the coat pocket, he returned to the King under the impression that the jewels were glass. But they kept the locket and chain which were recognizably gold.

* These words are the King's in his *Memoirs*. The actuality behind the simple statement may be inferred from the fact that when James, in 1692, issued an amnesty to all who had taken part against him, he expressly excepted from it Churchill and these men.

It was now day. The ringleader returned, but not to fulfil his promise. The hoy was taken across the Swale to the mouth of Faversham creek, where the three prisoners were made to land and make their way to a waiting coach. Sheldon, because of his apparent rank, and Hales, because of his lameness, were carried ashore; but James was made to walk in his riding boots through the ooze.

The coach took them to the Arms of England in Faversham and when they arrived at the inn James, who noticed that, despite his disguise and his black wig, several people knew him, took no further trouble to hide his identity. He sent a letter to the Lord Lieutenant of the county, who was at Canterbury, asking him to attend him with whatever Kentish gentlemen were with him, and announced his intention of staying in the meantime with the Mayor, who was known to be loyal. As he walked to the Mayor's house, he was surrounded by a shouting rabble of seamen who constituted themselves unofficial gaolers, lest he should try to escape. The Mayor welcomed him with all the comfort he could and, realizing that he was penniless, combined with the doctor, the vicar and the schoolmaster to present him immediately with thirty guineas.

James asked for pen and paper to write a short note to Lord Feversham: 'I had the misfortune to be stopped at Sheerness by a rabble of seamen, fisherman and others, who still detain me here, although they know me' and asked him to send down some linen, clothes, money and servants. As soon as this was dispatched to London, he went to his room for a rest.

His captors, however, were not inclined to allow it and a

crowd of them, ignoring the Mayor's protests, assembled outside his window to applaud while one of their number, with a stentorian voice, read slowly and pointedly William's Declaration. To escape this, James tried to move to another room, but found his door picketed by a grinning company of seamen.

He felt suddenly light-headed. He was no longer fully aware where he was or why, except that he was a prisoner.

'What have I done?' he asked them. 'Tell me the truth. What error have I committed?' Then he realized that, among the things that had been taken from him was St Edward the Confessor's Crucifix, containing a splinter of the Cross. He must tell them about it. Not, at the moment, about his loss, but about the Cross itself. They became quiet with surprise as, for half an hour, he preached to them. Then, suddenly his nose started to bleed again and the doctor ran to attend him and at last put him to bed.

As soon as the news of his capture reached London, Feversham, Ailesbury and Middleton (who had refused to have anything to do with the Council which had been set up) set out with three coaches and two regiments of Guards for Faversham. They found, as they came through Kent, that the Irish panic had spread there also and were only just in time to prevent the citizens of Rochester blowing up the bridge. When they arrived at their destination, Ailesbury rushed straight to the King. He found him, sitting in a large armchair with his hat on. As he had not shaved for a week, his beard had grown and his loss of blood had made him look white and drawn. For a moment Ailesbury went cold at the heart for he looked exactly like the famous portrait of his

father on trial before the revolutionary tribunal in Westminster Hall.

The room was filled with men, women and children all
talking as if they were at a fair. Ailesbury shouted them to
silence, and made what obeisance to James he could. But
because of his jack-boots he was not able to kneel and a
crook of the knee had to do duty for the proper formality.
He apologized for it.

'But you were all Kings when I left London!' said James,
amusedly.

Ailesbury's Scottish mind failed to see the point of the jest
and he thought the King was reproaching him.

'Is there anything particular that you want, sir?' he asked,
stiffly.

'Yes,' said James. 'A clean shirt.'

XXV

The King

WILLIAM had taken up residence in Windsor Castle when Feversham arrived with a letter from James, announcing his intention to return to London and inviting William to St James's to discuss matters. Even his intimates had never known him in a worse temper. He realized that, twenty-four hours before entering London as *de facto* King, his schemes had suddenly been brought to the edge of ruin. There was undeniably a revulsion in favour of James, which was hourly increasing as tales of his ill-treatment coursed through the country. Sober men, who had taken William at his word and credited him with no ambition, were now talking of an arrangement by which William should become his uncle's Admiral and Generalissimo. Sancroft, the moment he heard that the King was still on English soil, had refused to attend any more meetings of the self-constituted Council in London* and his stand increased the danger that the Church of England, even

---

* Sancroft's conversion by the events he had helped to precipitate was complete. He refused to take the oath of allegiance to William; and to Mary refused even his blessing until she had written to beg her father's pardon for her conduct.

though it had rejected James as a Catholic could not necessarily be relied on to support the Calvinistic Prince of Orange, whose hatred for it was no secret to some of its leaders.

The one thing that William had never envisaged was that James, if he were free to continue his way to Versailles, would return to London. When he had sent instructions to the Orange partisans in Faversham that the King was to be allowed his freedom, he had assumed that James would reembark and so solve for him his major problem. Now, if the King came back to the capital at this point, not only would he instead of William reap the relief of citizens still apprehensive from 'Irish Night,' but William might find it impossible to seize the throne without a fight. Men's loyalties were incalculable.

In a towering rage, which surprised even Bentinck, the Prince ordered Feversham to be put under arrest in the Round Tower for high treason in disbanding the army. The insult and the implication were calculated. Then he sent Zuylestein to James with peremptory orders to come no nearer London than Rochester.

But before Zuylestein reached him, James was already in London. He had left Rochester early on Sunday, December 15, ridden as far as Dartford, where he had dined and thence proceeded more slowly by coach. Vast crowds on horseback came to meet him from the city and the suburbs, and the roadsides were filled with spectators on foot. Blackheath was a mass of cheering citizens. Here two eminent merchants came to his coach to beg him not to go to Whitehall by barge but to ride through the city, where a welcome had been prepared for him. 'From St George's Southwark to Whitehall, a long march,' as a spectator reported, 'there was scarce room for the coaches to pass through and the balconies and windows were thronged, with loud acclamations beyond belief.' Bonfires were lighted, to honour instead of to exasperate him. Church bells rang and the mob huzzaed as loudly as it had so recently cried 'No Popery.' For his home-coming there were, as he noted, 'all imaginable marks of love and esteem.' He acknowledged them graciously, but he was quite unmoved. It was too late.

His scepticism was reinforced by his first encounter in Whitehall. The Earl of Mulgrave, his Lord Chamberlain, and the husband of one of his illegitimate daughters, having provided himself with a new wand of office to replace the one he had broken on hearing of the King's flight, requested a private interview.

James granted it with: 'My Lord, I am in a hurry to give an audience, so I trust that you will tell me quickly what you want.'

'To be made a marquess,' said Mulgrave.

'Good God!' said James. 'What a time to choose! I have hardly arrived, everything is in chaos and I don't even know whether I have a secretary.'

Mulgrave assured him that the absence of a secretary would make no difference and presented him with a patent for a marquisate which he had had already drawn up. As he was leaning against one of the doors, waiting for the King to sign it, Ailesbury opened the door from the outside to admit Zuylestein. Mulgrave fell backward into Ailesbury's arms but was propped up in time to hear James say angrily:

'I cannot do it. I will not do it.' With one glance at Zuylestein Mulgrave took the unsigned patent and hurried out to make his way to the Prince of Orange, where Schomberg received him with: 'So you have left the sinking ship!'

Zuylestein delivered William's message that James should approach no nearer than Rochester.

'That is now a little out of date,' said James, 'but my invitation remains that he should come to London. I will have apartments in St James's prepared for him.'

'He cannot come so long as it is garrisoned by your troops,' answered Zuylestein.

'Then let him bring his own guards,' said the King, answering the situation rather than the excuse, 'and I will dismiss mine. I am as well without any as with those I cannot trust.'

Zuylestein had hardly left the room when news of Feversham's arrest was brought to James, who sent at once to recall him. 'And add this message to your master,' said the King angrily. 'To detain a public minister sent with a royal message is against universal custom as well as against international law; so I trust that he will immediately release the Earl of Feversham.'

'The Earl of Feversham was given no safe conduct,' retorted Zuylestein, icily. 'In a state of war, such things are necessary.'

As there was no further doubt possible of William's intentions, James immediately summoned a Council, not because there was any business that could be done but so that, once more, he might assert, though he had no longer power to maintain, his Kingship. By Order in Council he officially ended the anarchy by directing all Lords-Lieutenant and other local officers to suppress riotous and tumultuous meetings.

Just before supper, he was told that the ringleader of the Sheerness boatmen had arrived at Whitehall and craved to see him. When the man was admitted, he immediately fell on his knees and begged the King's pardon, pleading that, had he the slightest suspicion of his identity, he would have helped him in every way.

'And here, Your Majesty,' he said, 'is all the money and the valuables you entrusted to me; but what was taken when I was away I cannot bring, for the rogues have fled and are in hiding.'

'And here,' said James, smiling, 'is your receipt. And ten pounds to drink my health!'

At supper, the King recounted his adventures at Faversham with as much unconcern as if they had happened to someone else. He addressed the recital mainly to the page who was waiting on him, Dartmouth's young son. He thought it improbable that he would again see Dartmouth, who was blockaded in Portsmouth, but he supposed the boy would report it one day.

At midnight, he heard Mass in his Chapel, in thanksgiving for the news just brought to him of the safe arrival in France of the Queen and Prince of Wales. When the eighty-year-old Earl of Craven, the Captain of his Guard and a Protestant, expressed some surprise at the hour, James explained that to hear Mass at midnight was a privilege which canon law allowed only to a Catholic King.

Next day, Monday, December 17, William called together at Windsor a council of those peers who had deserted to him to discuss what should be done. Clarendon was intentionally late. He had no wish to be a participator in events, and when Halifax started to tell him of the discussion, he interrupted with:

'If you have taken a decision there is no need to tell me anything.'

But Halifax was relentless. 'The Lords have decided that the King should be advised to leave Whitehall and go to the Duchess of Lauderdale's house at Ham.'

'Why should the King leave Whitehall?'

'The Prince of Orange does not believe he will be safe in London.'

William had, in fact, made it inescapably plain that he would not enter London as long as James was in it; and the Lords, fearing a repetition of the anarchy or even the outbreak of civil war, agreed with him. If William had to take London as a conqueror, there was no foreseeing what the end would be.

'But why,' persisted Clarendon, 'should the King go to Ham? Why can't he go where he likes—or at least to one of his own houses, Hampton Court or here at Windsor?'

The brutal and passionate Lord Delamere, one of the earliest of the conspirators, burst out: 'King! I don't own him as king. Why should he be allowed to choose? He must not go as King to one of his own houses. He must be *ordered* to Ham.'

William, who came into the room at this juncture, nodded at Delamere approvingly.

'That is well said, my lord. We shall so direct him.'

'Or better,' pursued Delamere, 'why do we not act on Lord Churchill's suggestion——'

Churchill looked at Halifax who interrupted quickly, speaking to William: 'May I ask, sir, that, as we have all spoken very freely here, it would be unwise if our deliberations were made known?'

'Certainly,' said William, who understood perfectly the reason for the request since he had privately been urged by Churchill to imprison James in the Tower, 'I enjoin secrecy on you all. And now we must decide who is to carry this message to my uncle.'

'The Count de Solmes,' suggested Halifax.

'It would come better, I think, from Englishmen. I will give you the honour, Lord Halifax—and you, Lord Shrewsbury—and you, Lord Delamere.'

At Whitehall, that morning, two young Scots presented themselves in the Presence Chamber—Colin Lindsay, Earl of Balcarres and John Graham of Claverhouse, Viscount Dundee. James welcomed them affectionately. Here at least were friends. Balcarres, when a youth of eighteen, had served under him at sea with such bravery that it had been specially rewarded; 'Bonnie' Dundee, whose beauty of face was as memorable as his reckless Highland courage, had been one of his trusted lieutenants in the government of Scotland. They had come, they said, charged with offers of service from his Privy Council in Scotland.

Immediately following them came another soldier, a

colonel who was still loyal but whom James recognized as a friend of Churchill's.

'I have come, your Majesty,' he said, 'to remind you that most of the officers of your Guards are still in London and that we have still power to serve and defend you. Though we are disbanded by your Majesty's order, you have but to bid your drums beat and you will have twenty thousand men before the end of the day.'

'I thank you, my lord, and I believe you to be a man of honour. But I know those who sent you are not,' said James. Then, suddenly, 'It's a good day. I'm going for a walk,' and went out alone.

He had the strange fancy to walk in the park and retrace the way which on a cold January morning, forty years ago all but a few weeks, his father had walked from St James's to the scaffold outside Whitehall; to see the same things under the same sky in the same frosty coldness on a day when he could understand as he had never understood before something of the murdered King's mind. He was standing in the Mall, looking at the window of the room in which the Prince of Wales had been born a brief six months before, when he realized that he was being followed. Turning quickly, he saw Dundee and Balcarres.

'What are you doing here?' he asked. 'You have taken the wrong direction. All wise men have gone to the Prince of Orange.'

'Would you insult us, sir,' said Dundee, 'by thinking we should have anything to do with him?'

'You once served under him,' said James.

'That was the occasion for his only good deed, sir—introducing me to your service.'

'You cannot doubt, sir,' said Balcarres, 'that we would both die for you.'

'Give me your hands on that, as men of honour.'

When they had done so, James said: 'You are indeed what I thought you and you shall know all my plans. I am going to France.'

'But why, sir, if we can——'

'My mind is made up. If I stay here, it will be either as a cipher or as the prisoner of the Prince of Orange, and you know there is only a short distance between the prisons and the graves of kings.'

'But we could still fight,' said Dundee.

'You are too good a soldier,' retorted James, 'not to know when the odds forbid anything but a massacre. If I brought that on the country, I should deserve its hatred. No, I am going to France; and when I am there I will send you my orders. You, Balcarres, I appoint to manage my civil affairs in Scotland and you, Dundee, Commander-in-Chief of my troops there.' There, in the cold Park they, grotesquely, kissed hands. 'And now, gentlemen,' said the King, 'though I shall from my heart welcome your company later, I wish to walk back to Whitehall alone.'

On his return he wrote a letter to Berwick. On the eve of his flight, he had sent his son down to Portsmouth with instructions to hold the town until he heard from him. It was an impossible assignment, for, though the garrison were loyal to their young Governor, there was no way of feeding the inhabitants. The Cromwellian Colonel Norton, with all the militia of the county, stiffened by a core of Dutch troops, had posted himself on the heights of Portsdown and cut off the land approach. And by sea the fleet ensured a complete blockade. When Berwick put the position to Dartmouth, the Admiral answered with tears in his eyes that there was nothing he would not do in the King's service but that, although all conventional honours were still being paid to him, he was a virtual prisoner, and his Rear-Admiral, Barry (who had long been in William's pay) was in command.

'My lord,' he added, as Berwick left, 'may I give you one piece of advice?'

'What is that?'

'Do not come on board again, lest they make you prisoner too.'

Berwick had therefore been forced to come to terms with Norton and promise that he would refrain from any hostile act, whatever the circumstances, provided that the Colonel, on his side, would allow the country people to bring their provisions into Portsmouth as usual.

James now determined that the farce must be ended; but it should be ended on his word and in such a way that none could mistake that William had committed an act of war. He ordered Berwick formally to surrender the town to Colonel Talmash and then to return, as quickly as he could, to London. He sent the letter 'Haste, haste, post-haste.'

There was now one last act of kingship left to do. That afternoon James touched a hundred poor men for King's Evil. Just before the ceremony started, he realized that he was still penniless and, since the ceremony demanded that a piece of gold should be bound by the King to the arm of each patient, he had to borrow a hundred guineas from Godolphin to enable him to perform it.

During the day, William had given instructions to his army, and as soon as it was dark, London found itself an occupied city. Paddington swarmed with Brandenburgers, and other German regiments under Birkenfeld took over Kensington; there were Holsteiners in Woolwich and a detachment of Scottish mercenaries in Lambeth; into West-minster itself poured six thousand Dutch, whom alone William would trust with the immediate defence of his person.

James was just going to bed when the Earl of Craven, in command of the Coldstreams who were on guard at White-hall, came to announce that the Count de Solmes, with three battalions of Dutch foot and some horse, were in the Park.

'They must have come to mount guard at St James's. The Prince of Orange is coming there tomorrow for a conference with me. I told Zuylestein he could have his own men there.'

'But they are outside Whitehall, sir.'

'Send for the Count,' said James, 'and I will explain his mistake.'

There was no mistake. Solmes presented the King with William's orders that the Dutch were to take possession of all places now occupied by the King's Guards, namely Whitehall, St James's and Somerset House. The King's Guards were to be dismissed.

'By God,' said Craven, drawing his sword, 'I am eighty years old, but I will be cut to pieces before I see a King of England a prisoner in his own palace.'

'My Lord,' said James, 'you drew that sword for my house long before I was born'—Craven, in his youth, had been a legendary knight-errant for James's aunt, the peerless Elizabeth of Bohemia—'and you must forgive me if I must seem harsh to your loyalty in commanding you to sheathe it.'

Craven managed to bow and, muttering curses, went off to dismiss his men, while James, with de Solmes's guards posted at his door, went to bed and fell unconcernedly to sleep.

He was awakened roughly about midnight by Halifax, Shrewsbury and Delamere who told him that he was to leave London before midday and retire to Ham.

Treating the news with a casual quietness which exasperated them, he merely remarked that Ham was cold, damp and unfurnished and that he would prefer to act on the Prince's original suggestion and go to Rochester.

'Our orders are peremptory,' said Halifax.

James looked at the man whom he had appointed as his own envoy so short a time ago and said: 'You trim your sails fast, my lord, but you are still my messenger. You will go back and tell my son, William, that I intend to go to Rochester.'

Tuesday brought a black sky and torrents of rain. When it was known that James was leaving for Rochester, the ambassadors and the few faithful English councillors came to take their leave of him. As a last mark of respect, they attended him to the water's edge when, from the private stairs of Whitehall, he entered the Royal Barge just before noon. Along the banks, defying the weather, Londoners crowded. Barillon noticed and reported to Louis: 'The English were very sorrowful at seeing him depart. Most of them had tears in their eyes. There was an appearance of consternation in the people when they found that their king was surrounded by Dutch guards and that he was, in fact, a prisoner.' William had insisted on that. Twelve boats, filled with Dutch soldiers, surrounded the barge. Of his own subjects, the King was allowed only five—Ailesbury and Dundee, with the Earls of Dumbarton, Lichfield and Arran.

The Dutch were so long embarking that they missed the tide and the King was forced to have his dinner on board. During it, he ordered a servant to hand over a dish of meat and some bottles of wine to the officer of the guards on the nearest boat.

'Rather throw him into the river,' muttered Arran.

James, overhearing, reproved him: 'My Lord, you are a very good subject, but a very bad Christian. The officer is a man of honour who is only doing his duty.'

Long before James made Gravesend, William entered London in state. The same crowds that had watched the King go watched the Prince arrive, as in the pouring rain he drove along Piccadilly, with Schomberg at his side. There were cheers and bells and sputtering bonfires but, as one observer noted, they did not at all equal those which had greeted James two days before. The weather, possibly, was to blame; it had drowned men's spirits. 'It is not to be imagined,' wrote Clarendon, 'what a damp there was upon all sorts of men throughout the town.' William himself felt it and

hurried into St James's without making any acknowledgment of the waiting spectators. The apartments which he
chose were those in which the Prince of Wales had been
born. He found Mulgrave, with his patent for his Marquisate,
already outside the door.

James spent the night at Gravesend and next day rode on
to Rochester. He had seldom in his life felt better, but
Ailesbury, who had not slept for four nights, was in such a
condition that the King insisted that he used the Royal coach.
Ailesbury, too exhausted to protest, fell asleep immediately,
only to be awakened by Dixie, the coachman, roaring at the
top of his voice: 'God damn Father Petre.' The imprecations
continued monotonously till Ailesbury put his head out and
asked Dixie: 'What harm has Father Petre done you?'

'But for him, sir,' shouted Dixie, 'we shouldn't be
here.'

'I won't argue that now,' said Ailesbury. 'And if you can't
be quiet, at least leave out the oaths.'

'I hope he's in Hell,' said Dixie.

'He's in France,' said Ailesbury and went to sleep again.

At Rochester, the King lodged with Sir Richard Head,
the garden of whose house sloped down to the river. He
could leave for France whenever he wished, since his escape
was the one point on which he and William were in complete agreement. Certainly he was still guarded, but the
soldiers were as ostentatiously in front of the house as they
were significantly absent from the back. Moreover, the
officer in charge and more than half the men were Catholics,

as James discovered when he had Mass celebrated in his host's largest room.

When it was ended, James remarked to the Dutch Colonel, who was the nephew of Sir Peter Lely, that it seemed odd that such an uproar had been raised because he had appointed a few Catholic officers.

'In my whole army of eighteen thousand men,' he said, 'I believe I had not a thousand Catholics.'

'At least two-thirds of our army are Catholics,' said the Colonel, 'but I fear most of them do not take their religion very seriously.'

James turned to a grizzled cavalry officer standing by: 'What religion are you?'

The officer drew his sword. 'By your leave, sir, *this* is my religion, and I fight well for those who pay me well.'

His face and voice touched a chord in James's memory.

'I am sure I have seen you before,' he said.

'Yes, indeed, sir. I had the honour to serve under your Majesty when you were Duke of York. It was thirty years ago—at Dunkirk.'

Permission to escape could hardly have been made plainer. Yet, for three days, James still waited. One thing was still missing . . .

In London, on the day after William's arrival, the weather changed. The rain disappeared and was succeeded by a hard frost and a clear, brilliant sky. Anne decided that, on such a day, she could make her entry into London an occasion to eclipse her brother-in-law's. She had discovered that she disliked him more than she could have imagined possible.

She was very sorry for Mary and she and Sarah were already referring to him as 'Caliban.' But she was, of course, extremely loyal and had had a new dress made for the occasion entirely of orange silk. She came to London from Windsor in her father's best carriage with Sarah Churchill sitting, and George of Denmark riding, beside her. She thought he looked more stupid than usual; but admittedly she was in a bad temper, because there were few people about, hardly anyone noticed her and nobody cheered.

On Sunday, December 22, Berwick at last arrived at Rochester. James could hardly contain his joy, for, as each day had brought no news, his fears had increased that his son had been arrested after he had surrendered Portsmouth.

'I came as quickly as I could,' Berwick explained, 'but I thought it best to come by by-ways.'

'Now you are here, James,' said the King, 'we will leave at once. All has been ready for the last forty-eight hours.'

That night before going to bed, James took farewell of Ailesbury.

'For the second time, my lord, I must leave you. Tonight you must not be on duty in my bedchamber. Dumbarton can take your place. He has nothing to lose or to fear.'

'But you doubt my loyalty no longer, sir?'

'It is because of your loyalty that I order this. On all occasions and in the worst times, you have stuck by me so firmly that I should be ashamed if now I did not think of your safety. If you are in my room tonight, they may torture you in London to make you tell what happens.'

'I should not break ... But why, sir, may I not come with you?'

'Because I need you here. I shall come back, but while I am away you can serve me better in one day by being here on the spot than you could in years in France.'

Ailesbury argued no more.

About midnight, James and Berwick—the father dressed as the son's servant—left their room, accompanied by Labadie, who was by now experienced in escapes, and one Gentleman of the Bedchamber, and stole quietly down the garden to the riverside where Captain Trevannion was waiting for them with a boat, to take them to his smack lying off Sheerness.

With wind and tide against them it was six in the morning before they reached the smack's moorings, and they had to wait till daybreak before they could find her, for the gale had forced her to change her position. Though the wind was still blowing with almost hurricane force, the King insisted on boarding her. He was still a sailor hard to match in England and, with the sound and smell of the sea about him, the last burden had fallen away from his spirit.

The cabin was so small that there was scarcely room for him and Berwick to sit there, for both were long-legged; but this discomfort was ease enough. And the meal the Captain provided was luxury. The frying-pan had a hole in it, which Trevannion had to stop with a pitched rag before he could fry the bacon, and the only available drinking vessel was a split and mildewed cup, which had to be cleaned and tied round with a cord before the beer was poured in.

James roared with laughter at the Captain's attempts to

appear unconcerned, but assured him, with absolute truth, that he had never enjoyed a meal so much in his life.

Failing to make Calais, they put in at Ambleteuse. It was the dawn of Christmas Day and the countryside was white with snow. In the distance a church bell was ringing. With arms linked, James and his son set off for the Mass of Christ.

Author's Note

I have tried to portray James and the events of the last six months of 1688 as accurately as possible, and this book is based on two years' research. It is an 'historical novel' in the sense that it is an attempt to convey the historical truth in a more concentrated manner than is possible in academic history (which is also a form—and I should contend, a lower form—of fiction).

Since many readers may be familiar with the reign only through the vivid fictional pages of Macaulay, I may add that, on the professional level, there is no reliable or accurate account of 1688, though Professor L. Pinkham's *William III and the Respectable Revolution* (Harvard University Press, 1954) attempts at least to put it in its proper perspective and K. H. D. Haley's *William of Orange and the English Opposition, 1672–4* (Oxford University Press, 1953), by explaining the first phase of the intrigue, increases understanding of the last.

No reader should approach any book on James II and his reign without first studying Malcolm V. Hay's *The Enigma of James II* (Sands and Co., 1938) which, with careful documentation, disposes of many of the deliberate untruths propagated by academic historians. This important book, understandably neglected by English historians (whose bona fides it amiably destroys) is recognized by Continental writers.